Brain *S E N S E*

A Guide and Workbook to Keep Your Mind and Memory Sharp

Linda Sasser, Ph.D.

Brain and Memory Health

Contents

Introduction

How old would you be if you didn't know how old you was?
Satchel Paige

Evidence from research indicates that healthy older adults without dementia are sometimes able to maintain and even improve their cognitive skills, especially memory, through training. One aim of this book is to help people understand the importance of brain health and what research is suggesting we do to maintain the health of our brain. The other purpose is to engage the reader in cognitive exercises to maintain or even improve thinking and memory skills and/or to slow decline in these skills that may occur with normal aging.

In a groundbreaking study, older adults who received as few as 10 sessions of mental training not only improved their cognitive functioning in daily activities in the months after the training but continued to show long-lasting improvements 10 years later. The Advanced Cognitive Training for Independent and Vital Elderly (ACTIVE) study involved 2,832 people with an average age of 74. They participated in 60 to 75-minute training sessions in memory, reasoning, or speed of processing, using exercises such as memorizing lists, detecting patterns in number series, and operating a touch-screen program. Ten years later, about 70 to 75 percent of the participants who had received training were still performing tasks above their pre-trial baseline level, compared to about 62 and 49 percent of those who did not receive training (Rebok et al., 2014).

Many people experience memory glitches as they age, and as a result often believe either that their memory is declining, or worse, that they are developing Alzheimer's disease. This belief can lead them to lose confidence in their ability to remember, resulting in lower self-efficacy. One's sense of self-efficacy is related to belief in one's ability to succeed at certain tasks, and it can influence how one approaches challenges. Research indicates that memory skills training and self-efficacy training regarding memory and cognitive function are effective in improving both people's memory ability and their confidence in it. Participants reported that they used memory strategies acquired through the training up to 51 percent of the time in their everyday lives, and follow-up assessment found that cognitive gains were often maintained at least six months after training (McDougall, 2009). Engaging in mindfulness, relaxation, and stress reduction practices can also contribute to these benefits.

Research has demonstrated that older adults who learn and then use memory strategies show improvement in keeping track of items and remembering names and faces, and that they have more confidence in their memory ability (Fairchild & Scogin, 2010). Frequent participation in cognitively stimulating activities is associated with reduced risk of Alzheimer's disease (Wilson et al., 2002). Training of this nature has also been found to benefit individuals with Mild Cognitive Impairment (MCI) (Rapp, Brenes, & Marsh, 2002). MCI is characterized by memory problems which are not severe enough to interfere with activities of daily living, but which are greater than the those typically experienced as part of normal aging.

Since one change that often accompanies aging is a decrease in cognitive *processing speed* (how quickly we can think and respond), some activities in this book target your reaction time and automatic responses. Due to the shrinkage of the frontal lobes with aging, exercises to improve skills involving attention and concentration are emphasized; these in turn can help your memory. Training in concentration uses divided attention and selective processing exercises to enhance listening and information processing skills.

In addition to an explanation of how memory works, *mnemonic* strategies are included to help you move information through the memory network from short-term to long-term. You will learn how to use strategies such as rehearsal, association, categorization, and imagery. You will also learn techniques for remembering names, numbers, tasks, and other information. Research indicates that older adults benefit from strategies involving visual imagery because the occipital region of the brain, responsible for visual information processing, does not deteriorate with age as much as the frontal lobes (Gross et al., 2012). Visual imagery is useful for list-learning, prospective memory (remembering to do things in the future), and other types of memory. External memory aids, such as to-do lists, calendars, and post-it notes, make use of environmental cues that assist with recall, especially of prospective memory tasks (Caprio-Prevette et al., 1996).

Language activities are included to increase fluency and word retrieval for improved communication. Reasoning exercises sharpen analytical and critical thinking. Problem solving strategies, from correctly understanding and representing a problem to formulating possible solutions, are also included, along with exercises to enhance creative thinking.

Answers to the exercises in this book can be found in the **Answers to Exercises** chapter at the end of the book.

A Partial List of Cognitive Processes

- *Attention* — the ability to selectively focus and concentrate on one aspect of your surroundings while disregarding others
- *Auditory Short-term Memory* — the ability to remember, for a brief time, information that is heard
- *Inhibition* — the ability to ignore irrelevant stimuli or suppress irrelevant responses while performing a task (i.e., the ability to not get distracted)
- *Long-term Memory* — the brain's system for storing (for a long period of time), managing, and retrieving information for later use
- *Planning* — the ability to "think ahead," to mentally anticipate the way to execute a task
- *Problem Solving* — the process of finding solutions to difficult or complex issues
- *Processing Speed* — the rate at which the brain can perceive information, process it, and respond, or the ability to fluently perform easy or over-learned cognitive tasks
- *Reaction Time* — the ability to perceive and process a simple stimulus and respond to it
- *Reasoning* — the process of drawing inferences or conclusions from facts or premises
- *Short-term Memory* — the ability to hold a small amount of information in a readily available state for a short period of time
- *Visual Short-term Memory* — the ability to briefly remember information that is seen
- *Working Memory* — the ability to temporarily store and manipulate information necessary for complex cognitive tasks

Building Cognitive Reserve

Cognitive reserve refers to the brain's ability to perform cognitive tasks adequately despite neuropathological (brain) damage, and is also related to *neuroplasticity*, or the brain's ability to develop and maintain extra neurons and connections. Later in life these connections may help compensate for the rise in dementia-related brain pathology (disease) that accompanies aging. Education, mentally demanding occupations, and cognitively stimulating activities are all thought to increase cognitive reserve (Stern, 2009; LaRue, 2010).

It is believed that continuing to stimulate the brain with novel and complex ideas, and continuing to learn, increases cognitive reserve and the number of connections between neurons. Studies have demonstrated that greater cognitive reserve is associated with better cognitive performance and a reduced risk of developing dementia in healthy elderly people. Since cognitive reserve can be improved at almost any age, engaging in cognitively stimulating activities may improve your brain health and possibly prevent or at least postpone cognitive decline (Tucker & Stern, 2011).

DISCLAIMER: Though research studies have shown that sufficient time spent on exercises of the type included in this book have helped people without brain disorders maintain cognitive function, <u>no claim</u> is being made by this author that the exercises in this book are *guaranteed* to boost brain power, increase memory, or prevent cognitive decline. Also, this book is intended for people without cognitive impairment, and the exercises are designed to be challenging. Readers should not expect to be able to succeed at all the exercises or solve all the problems. Attempting them, however, stimulates cognitive functions, which may improve brain health.

Chapter One
Meet Your Marvelous Brain

It seems that everyone, everywhere, is concerned about brain health. Whether because they are over 50 and concerned for themselves, or under 50 and concerned for aging parents or relatives, most people are beginning to realize that taking care of the brain is as important as taking care of the body, if not more so. Since the brain controls everything you do, if it is not healthy all your functions will be affected.

In this chapter, you will learn about some of your brain's structures and functions, from neurons and neurotransmitters to the hippocampus and amygdala. You will also learn about *neuroplasticity*, or how the brain changes in response to our experiences, along with findings from recent research which indicate that *neurogenesis* (the creation of new neurons) can occur even in adult brains.

Do You Know... (Be on the lookout for the answers as you read this chapter.)
1. How many neurons, or brain cells, your brain has?
2. How much your brain weighs?
3. Whether your brain can generate new brain cells?

Have you ever wondered about all the marvelous things your brain does? Our brain is more complex than the most sophisticated computer we have ever used. Most of us only notice our brain when its functions are not working as well as we would like. We can't think, move, talk, eat, sleep, dream, or learn without using the brain. This is one reason it is so important that we do everything we can to take care of it! Recent research has provided many insights regarding the impact of behavior on the brain, so there is no excuse for not following the practical guidance available to keep the brain functioning optimally as we age.

Brain Basics

Below are some of the major components of the brain, along with their functions. The outer wrinkly covering of the brain is called the *cortex* and is divided into four types of lobes.

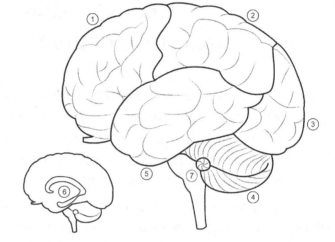

1. The **frontal lobes**, at the front of the brain, control executive functions such as planning, decision making, and reasoning. *If you count backwards from 100 by 7, you are using your frontal lobes.*

2. The **parietal lobes**, at the top of the cortex, receive and process sensory information from the body. *If you pinch yourself (gently, of course!) the sensation is experienced in your parietal lobes.*

3. The **occipital lobes**, at the back of the brain, process incoming visual information. Visualize a place you like to visit. *Though you are only "seeing" it in your mind's eye, your occipital lobes are processing this image.*

4. The **cerebellum** coordinates balance, movement, and posture. *Whenever you walk, dance, or ride a bicycle, your cerebellum is at work.*

5. The **temporal lobes** process incoming auditory information (and also include the limbic system described below). *Pause and listen to whatever sounds are around you; this will activate your temporal lobes.*

6. The **limbic system** is comprised of the **amygdala** (pronounced *a-MIG-da-la*), the brain's emotion center, and the **hippocampus**, which sends memories of facts and spatial relationships to the appropriate part of the cerebral hemisphere for long-term storage and retrieves them when necessary. *If you recall your last birthday, you are activating your hippocampus; if you think about someone you love, you are activating your amygdala.*

7. The **brain stem**, which connects to the spinal cord, controls functions basic to survival, such as heart rate, breathing, digestion and sleep. These functions are referred to as *autonomic*, meaning we have no control over them—they occur involuntarily.

The brain contains about one-hundred billion nerve cells (neurons), which have about one-hundred trillion connections between them. Neurons have branch-like structures called *dendrites*, which bring information to the cell body, and *axons*, which take information away from the cell body. Some axons are covered with a fatty substance called *myelin* that acts as an insulator and allows for faster transmission of information.

Chemicals in the brain set off electrical impulses between neurons. The brain produces about enough electricity to power a small light bulb. The chemicals, called *neurotransmitters*, flow in the *synapses* (gaps) between the neurons. Information flows from neuron to neuron across the synapses, and the connections established result in our ability to remember, among other functions.

The brain is comprised of two fairly symmetrical *hemispheres*, the left and right sides of the brain, which are connected by a bundle of nerve fibers called the *corpus callosum*. The left brain contains regions involved primarily in speech and language and is also associated with mathematical calculations and the retrieval of facts. The right brain is more visual and intuitive and is mainly involved in spatial processing and creativity. Although the two sides function differently, they work together and complement each other.

Brain Break

I have discovered what is wrong with my brain: on the left side there is nothing right, and on the right side there is nothing left.

For most adults, the brain's weight comprises only about 2% of body mass. However, it uses 20% or more of our body's energy output. It needs fuel (*oxygen* and *glucose*) to operate, meaning we should exercise to increase oxygen intake and eat a balanced diet to regulate glucose. Since the brain, like our body, is mostly water, adequate *hydration* is also necessary for effective cognitive processing.

Each new experience we have changes the brain, for better or for worse. This adaptability is called *neuroplasticity*, which refers to the brain's ability to form new neural connections throughout life in response to new information, sensory stimulation, and development. Though plasticity continues throughout life, it is most evident in our early developmental years. For adults, this process enables neurons to compensate for injury or disease, such as when one hemisphere begins performing functions previously carried out by the other hemisphere.

The ability to view the brain through various scanning methodologies (fMRI, PET) enables scientists to observe its processes as well as changes in structure and function. fMRI stands for *functional* magnetic resonance imaging; it measures the small changes in blood flow that occur with brain activity. Positron Emission Tomography (PET) measures functions such as blood flow, oxygen use, and glucose (blood sugar) metabolism, and can show activity in different regions of the brain during cognitive processing. PET scans can be used to evaluate changes in cognitive abilities, including detecting the decline in glucose metabolism associated with decreased cognitive function.

In a study of students learning a foreign language, MRIs showed that after three months of intensive study the learners' hippocampi grew measurably. Those who had worked harder to speak the language fluently also had greater growth in the cortex's motor region, related to mouth movements. A study in Germany showed that people who spent three months learning to juggle had greater volume in the parietal cortex regions important for sensory motor integration. Three months after they had stopped juggling, their gray matter volume decreased, indicating that the parts of the brain responsible for movements used in juggling grew larger with practice and then shrank with disuse (Fotuhi, 2013).

Much like satellite navigation found in cars, the brain has a navigation system with the equivalent of maps, grids and compasses, according to neuroscientist Hugo Spiers at University College London. This navigation mechanism resides in the hippocampus, which is responsible for learning and memory. A study carried out by Eleanor Maguire, also at University College, found a region of the hippocampus was enlarged in London taxi drivers compared to the general population. Bus drivers, who were matched for driving experience and levels of stress, did not have the same enlarged area. The authors speculated that the difference in hippocampus size is related to the fact that London taxi drivers must study and learn *The Knowledge,* a compendium of the city's 250,000 streets, to navigate across the entire region, while bus drivers generally follow a constrained set of routes. In addition, years of navigation experience correlated with hippocampal gray matter volume only in taxi drivers. The authors speculated that the taxi drivers' hippocampi grew as their brains updated the spatial representations of their routes. The results provide evidence that extensive practice with spatial navigation affects the hippocampus and results in structural differences in the brain (Maguire et al., 2000, Maguire, et al., 2006). This is an excellent example of *neuroplasticity*, or how the brain changes in response to our experiences.

Sommeliers (wine stewards) spend years learning about the geography, chemistry, history and of course, the smells of specific wines. They must pass a rigorous exam process which includes blind tasting, so they need to use their memory for both information and odor. According to the Court of Master Sommeliers, at the time of this writing there were only 255 Master Sommeliers worldwide. In a study published in 2016, researchers at the Cleveland Clinic in Las Vegas compared brain scans of 13 sommeliers with those of 13 people with other types of jobs. The researchers found that sections of the sommeliers' brains dealing with the olfactory (smell) network and areas dealing with memory were thicker. These differences show that neuroplasticity continues throughout life, therefore supporting the theory that lifestyle choices and practices play a major role in how our brains change and function (Banks et. al., 2016).

> *I don't know why my brain has kept all the words to the Gilligan's Island theme song and has deleted everything about triangles.*
>
> Jeff Foxworthy

One way in which the brain changes involves *neurogenesis*, or the formation and development of nerve cells. For most of the twentieth century, the consensus was that brain cells could not renew themselves once the developmental period was over. In the 1960s Altman discovered that new neurons are generated in the brains of adult mammals (in this case, rats), specifically in a hippocampus area known to be crucial for memory. In the 1990s improved techniques for visualizing brain cells resulted in wider acceptance of adult neurogenesis. At the Karolinska Institute in Stockholm, Frisén and his colleagues estimated that about 1,400 hippocampal neurons are made daily in adult human brains (Frisén, 2013).

In a 2018 study, Maura Boldrini, psychiatrist at Columbia University, found that we continue to develop new brain cells well into our 70s. She and her team (Boldrini et al., 2018) studied autopsied brains of individuals aged 14 to 79 whose medical records indicated no history of psychiatric diagnoses or chronic illness such as strokes or microvascular brain disease. They found the number of newborn neurons in the hippocampus to be only slightly fewer in the older adults than in younger individuals. The researchers suggested that healthy elderly people have the potential to remain cognitively and emotionally more intact than commonly believed due to the persistence of adult hippocampal neurogenesis (AHN) into the eighth decade of life (Boldrini et al., 2018).

However, whether and to what extent adult neurogenesis occurs in humans remains controversial. A study by Sorrells et al. (2018) using a different technique found that, unlike in other mammals, the human hippocampus does not generate new neurons after childhood. So amidst the 21st century presumption that hippocampal neurogenesis extends through adult life, the only thing now clear is that more research is needed.

Brain Break (See Answer #1, page 137)
(NOTE: ***Answers to Exercises*** are at the back of this book.)
Can you guess the answer to each of these riddles?
1. What does a brain do when it sees a friend across the street?
2. What did the hippocampus say during its retirement speech?
3. What do you get when you cross a thought with a light bulb?
4. Why do neurons like email?
5. If your dog was a neurologist, what would he do all day?

Keeping our brains active and engaged in new learning helps build *cognitive reserve*. Individuals with greater cognitive reserve are likely to do better after neurological injury due to having a greater number of frequently used brain areas. The brain has some redundancy, with multiple areas performing similar cognitive functions. If one area is disabled, a redundant area could be recruited to accomplish the injured area's task. Later in life, connections between enriched areas in a brain with high cognitive reserve may help compensate for the effects of dementia-related brain pathology. Yaakov Stern at Columbia University discovered that some people's brains, at autopsy, have the plaques and tangles of Alzheimer's disease, even though these people never exhibited symptoms. He attributes this to their having cognitive reserve (Stern, 2009). Research indicates that people with greater cognitive reserve are less likely to exhibit the classic signs of dementia, such as short-term memory loss or difficulty generating words, even if their brain scans indicate areas of damage. This is because cognitive reserve enables the brain to compensate for disease-related loss of functioning.

Research suggests that lifestyle changes, such as engaging in complex, challenging mental activities, may help develop cognitive reserve even when begun later in life (Stern, 2012). This training results in changes in brain structure and communication between brain cells (Wilson, 2011). In one study more than 1,000 men and women with an average age of 80, and without Alzheimer's disease or other forms of dementia, were given annual memory tests. They also completed questionnaires about how often they did things like reading the newspaper, writing letters, visiting the library or playing board games. The participants who regularly engaged in such mentally stimulating tasks had slower rates of decline in memory and thinking skills. The researchers also found they could predict how well someone would do on memory tests by looking at their levels of engagement in mentally stimulating activities the previous year (Wilson et al., 2012).

A brain with cognitive reserve is sometimes referred to as an "enriched" brain. The challenge of learning new information or procedures requires the brain to create new neural pathways and results in an increase in dendrites (branches extending from neurons) to create more connections between brain cells. As Arnold Scheibel, head of UCLA's Brain Research Institute stated, "Anything that's intellectually challenging can probably serve as a kind of stimulus for dendritic growth, which means it adds to the computational reserves in your brain." Trying to learn about or do things that are new to you can help build cognitive reserve. For example, a computer programmer might try sculpture; a ballerina might try marine navigation.

There is a growing body of research suggesting that cognitive reserve leading to better cognitive function in later life is associated not only with engagement in mentally stimulating activities, but also with engagement in complex work environments. One such study examined the relationship between the complexity of main lifetime occupation and cognitive performance in later years. They found that complexity of work with people and data were associated with greater cognitive performance at age 70 (Smart et al., 2014). Another study looked at people at risk for Alzheimer's disease, and found that greater occupational complexity appeared to provide resilience to the adverse effects of neuropathology on cognition (Boots et al., 2015). The "Complexity of Work" study from the Canadian Study of Health and Aging, involving 3,557 subjects over ten years, looked at the nature of work, and whether the occupation involves things (construction, manufacturing), people (human resources, education), or data (programming, financial analysis). This study concluded that a high complexity of work reduced the risk of dementia by an average of 27% for jobs involving things and 34% for jobs involving people. The study showed that length of time (in years) a person spent in a complex career was also important. For long-term jobs involving things, the risk for dementia was lowered by 55%, and for Alzheimer's it was lowered by 52%. If the long-term careers involved people, the risk for dementia and Alzheimer's was reduced by 64% and 69%, respectively (Kroeger et al., 2008).

Chapter Two
Mild Cognitive Impairment and Alzheimer 's Disease

Review of Chapter One
1. Which part of the brain is primarily responsible for memory, for emotion? (p. 2)
2. What does *neuroplasticity* mean, and why is it a good thing? (p. 3)
3. Describe *cognitive reserve.* How does cognitive reserve help the brain compensate for pathology? (p. 6)

This chapter discusses the differences between Mild Cognitive Impairment (MCI) and Alzheimer's disease, and memory difficulties that stem from often treatable conditions. It also discusses modifiable risk factors which may help in postponing onset of dementia or even prevent it (Yaffe, 2018). The trajectory of cognitive abilities as we age differs depending upon numerous factors. Although there are milestones for early childhood development, there are no equivalent norms for aging as cognition varies depending upon education, cultural influences, medical conditions and numerous other factors. If you are reading this book and worrying about your cognitive abilities, you are more likely experiencing a condition called Mild Cognitive Impairment (MCI) than a dementia process.

> *Unquestionably, the brain is our most precious physical possession, the seat of our entire being—our intelligence, personality, our humanity, our mind, our soul.*
> *Nothing is more central to a successful and fulfilling life*
> *than an optimally functioning brain.*
> Jean Carper

Mild Cognitive Impairment (MCI)

Mild Cognitive Impairment (MCI) is defined as a decline in thinking skills beyond normal age-related cognitive changes but not interfering enough with daily functioning to meet criteria for dementia. These mild but measurable changes in thinking abilities are usually noticeable to the person affected and to family members, friends, and coworkers. Though people with MCI may experience mild challenges in performing daily activities, the cognitive changes rarely interfere significantly with shopping, cooking, cleaning, completing hobbies, managing money, keeping appointments, or following medication schedules.

According to the Banner Alzheimer's Institute, approximately 14-18% of people over the age of 70 have been diagnosed with MCI. *Amnestic* MCI, meaning MCI involving memory problems, is the most common form. A diagnosis of MCI increases the risk for later developing dementia, but MCI can remain stable or revert to normal cognition. About 10-15% of those diagnosed with MCI will progress to dementia within the first year, while approximately 50% will develop dementia within five years (Anderson, Murphy, & Troyer, 2012).

Some additional information about MCI:

- There are currently no tests or procedures to demonstrate conclusively that a person has MCI, so MCI remains a "clinical" diagnosis representing a doctor's best professional judgment about the reason for a person's symptoms.
- Neuropsychological testing can compare a person's performance on memory tasks, processing speed, and other cognitive skills to others in the same age range and educational level to determine if and what declines have occurred.
- Some individuals diagnosed with MCI may remain stable or even improve, especially if they engage in cognitive interventions.

A study published in the journal *Neurology* (Wilson et. al., 2010) found that the thinking skills of people with amnestic MCI and other cognitive problems declined twice as fast each year as those without cognitive problems, whose thinking skills may have declined only slightly due to normal aging. In those with Alzheimer's disease, thinking skills declined four times as fast as those without notable cognitive problems.

Sandy Bem, a Cornell psychology professor, received a diagnosis of amnestic mild cognitive impairment (aMCI) at around age 65. In a document she entitled, "Memoir," she described the maddening capriciousness of "a mind that could be so alive one moment with thought and feeling building toward a next step and then someone erases the blackboard. It's all gone, and I can't even reconstruct what the topic was. It's just gone. And I sit with the dark, the blank" (Henig, 2015).

An apt illustration of the difference between memory deficits seen in normal aging, MCI, and Alzheimer's disease is provided by Fotuhi (2013), who shares a story about someone's memory of attending a party. A person with age-related memory changes would be able to describe a person he had spoken with at the party and a great deal about her, except for her name. A person with MCI might only remember talking to many people, with no detailed memory of anyone in particular. A person with Alzheimer's disease, in contrast, might respond, "What party?"

Dementia

Dementia is an umbrella term referring to deterioration in thinking severe enough to affect day-to-day functioning. Not all dementia is due to Alzheimer's, but everyone with Alzheimer's has dementia. Memory is not as impaired in some forms of dementia, although the decline of other functions makes retrieval less reliable. Alzheimer's is the most common cause of dementia among people age 65 and older. However, the term *Alzheimer's* is often used incorrectly to refer to different conditions that impair memory in older individuals. More than a hundred different disorders cause dementia, and their different symptoms depend on what parts of the brain they attack.

The term *dementia* refers to a group of symptoms resulting from a variety of conditions that cause nerve cells in the brain (*neurons*) to die or function abnormally. The resulting symptoms include impairment of memory, judgment, motor skills, word-finding and ability to think logically and flexibly. Deterioration may be slow or rapid, depending on the cause of dementia, where in the brain the damage has occurred, and how many neurons are affected.

Diagnosis of dementia depends upon who is making it. The term "dementia" has long been used to describe cognitive difficulties affecting ability to function effectively. The family physician will diagnose according to the International Statistical Classification of Diseases and Health Related Problems that is put out by the World Health Organization. As it is in its 10th edition, the list of conditions is referred to as ICD-10. It continues to use the term "dementia."

Mental health practitioners—including psychiatrists (who have the medical degrees of M.D. or D.O.) and psychologists (who have the doctoral degrees of Ph.D. or Psy.D.)—use the Diagnostic and Statistical Manual of Mental Disorders. Its Fourth Edition (DSM-IV) used the term "dementia," but its current Fifth Edition (DSM-5) uses the term "neurocognitive disorder" with requirement that the diagnosis be accompanied with the cause (e.g. Alzheimer's disease, frontotemporal lobe degeneration, vascular disease, Parkinson's disease, etc.). According to DSM-5, the diagnosis of Major Neurocognitive Disorder requires the following criteria:

A. Evidence of significant cognitive decline from a previous level of performance in one or more cognitive domains (complex attention, executive function, learning and memory, language, perceptual-motor, or social cognition) based on:

1. Concern of the individual, a knowledgeable informant, or the clinician that there has been a significant decline in cognitive function, and
2. A substantial impairment in cognitive performance, preferably documented by standardized neuropsychological testing or, in its absence, another quantified clinical assessment.

B. The cognitive deficits interfere with independence in everyday activities (i.e., at a minimum, requiring assistance with complex instrumental activities of daily living such as paying bills or managing medications).
C. The cognitive deficits do not occur exclusively in the context of a delirium.
D. The cognitive deficits are not better explained by another mental disorder (e.g., major depressive disorder, schizophrenia).

Potential Indicators of Dementia

- Memory loss, especially of recent events, names, placement of objects, and new information
- Confusion about time and place
- Difficulty completing familiar actions (e.g., brushing teeth)
- Difficulties with complex mental tasks (e.g., balancing checkbook)
- Trouble finding appropriate words, completing sentences, following directions/conversations
- Poor judgment when making decisions
- Changes in personality, mood swings, suspicion, withdrawal, disinterest in usual activities

What is Alzheimer's Disease?

Alzheimer's disease (AD) is an age-related, non-reversible brain disorder that develops over a period of years. Alzheimer's disease tends to appear initially as a rapid decline in memory and thinking skills including attention, visual and spatial awareness, and judgment. Often, people who are developing AD begin having difficulties with tasks which were once easy for them, such as balancing a checkbook or following a recipe. In most people with Alzheimer's, symptoms first appear in their mid-60s; however, early-onset Alzheimer's can strike people younger than 65. Some people with early-onset Alzheimer's have the common form of the disease, but others have a type that runs in families and is linked to three genes. These three genes account for less than one percent of all Alzheimer's disease cases but about 60 to 70 percent of early-onset Alzheimer's cases.

According to the Alzheimer's Association, the disease "eventually destroys synapses and kills neurons, damaging the brain's communication network which leads to a loss of thinking and memory capabilities." Alzheimer's progresses differently in each person, depending in part on the person's age and health, resulting in a wide range of life expectancies for those diagnosed with it. AD ultimately causes death, but the time it takes can be as short as three or as long as 20 years. No known cure exists for Alzheimer's, but according to the National Institute on Aging there are five drugs approved by the FDA to treat this disease. These drugs typically slow progression and work to improve, albeit temporarily, the cognitive and behavioral symptoms.

Analogy

If you think of memory as a photo album, Alzheimer's disease is when you stop putting in new photos and begin to delete old ones.

Initially, people experience memory loss and confusion, which may be mistaken for the kinds of memory changes sometimes associated with normal aging. However, the symptoms of AD gradually lead to behavior and personality changes, a decline in cognitive abilities such as decision-making and language skills, and problems recognizing family and friends. Alzheimer's disease ultimately leads to a severe loss of mental function due to the breakdown of the connections between certain neurons in the brain and the eventual death of those neurons.

When Alzheimer's affects the brain, people begin to lose their ability to
- remember recent events or conversations
- plan, start, or organize tasks
- find the right words or name everyday things, such as a clock or a stove
- comprehend or follow even simple directions
- keep track of the time and where they are

The severity and the speed of the memory loss distinguishes Alzheimer's from aging; yet the line between where normal aging ends and Alzheimer's begins is as unclear as the memories of a person with Alzheimer's. In Alzheimer's disease, the brain changes eventually impair an individual's ability to carry out such basic bodily functions as walking and swallowing – becoming ultimately fatal.

The Statistics on Alzheimer's Disease in the United States

According to the Alzheimer's Association, as of 2019, an estimated 5.8 million Americans are living with Alzheimer's disease; 81 percent of these are age 75 or older. This number is expected to rise to 14 million by the year 2050.

- One in ten people age 65 and older (10 percent) has Alzheimer's dementia.
- Almost two-thirds of Americans with Alzheimer's are women.
- Alzheimer's disease is the sixth-leading cause of death in the United States, and the fifth-leading cause of death among those age 65 and older.
- Nearly one in every three seniors who dies each year has Alzheimer's or another dementia.
  (www.alz.org/alzheimers-dementia/facts-figures)

Normal Cognitive Changes	Potential Indicators of Dementia
Sometimes misplaces keys, glasses, other items	Forgets what an item is used for or puts it in an inappropriate place
Momentarily forgets an acquaintance's name	May not remember knowing a person
Occasionally has to "search" for a word	Starts losing language skills; may withdraw from social interaction
Occasionally forgets to run an errand	Loses sense of time/day
May forget an event from the distant past	Difficulty learning and remembering new information

Potentially Treatable Causes of Memory Difficulties

Various factors other than Alzheimer's disease or another type of dementia can contribute to memory difficulties. Sometimes medical or psychological conditions impact memory function; when those are correctly diagnosed and treated, memory often improves. Some of these are described below. Dementia symptoms rarely, if ever, appear suddenly. If decline in cognitive functions, such as memory, occurs within a week or month, look for one of the causes shown below.

Medications and/or their interaction

Certain medications, including some sold over-the-counter, can negatively impact memory function. In addition, cognitive problems may result from medications interacting with each other. Many prescribed and over-the-counter drugs or combinations of drugs have memory loss as a side effect, especially in older adults' bodies, which tend to break down and absorb medication more slowly.

Common medications that affect memory and brain function include sleeping pills, antihistamines, blood pressure and arthritis medication, muscle relaxants, anticholinergic drugs for urinary incontinence and gastrointestinal discomfort, antidepressants, anti-anxiety meds, and painkillers. If you notice problems after starting a new medication, consult your doctor or pharmacist.

Depression, stress, and/or anxiety

Depression in older adults can result from retirement, a serious medical diagnosis, the loss of a loved one, or moving from a familiar environment. Depression can mimic the signs of memory loss, making it difficult to concentrate, stay organized, remember things, and accomplish tasks.

Stress and anxiety can also lead to memory difficulties. Stress is generally accompanied by the release of cortisol in the brain, and this hormone can wreak havoc with neurons and neuronal connections. Anxiety is especially detrimental to short-term memory, which can only hold a limited number of items, concepts, or thoughts. If a person is consumed with anxious and worrisome thoughts, these may interfere with registering and processing new information. In other words, if you're thinking "I'll never remember all this," you may not be hearing everything you need to recall. If it isn't encoded into memory in the first place, you can't retrieve it later.

Dehydration

Older adults are particularly susceptible to dehydration. Severe dehydration can cause confusion, drowsiness, memory loss, and other symptoms that mimic dementia. It is generally recommended to drink six to eight glasses of water per day to stay hydrated.

Estrogen decrease at menopause

The decrease in estrogen levels that accompany menopause can impact brain function and can also lead to anxiety, depression, and hot flashes - conditions that may contribute to memory difficulties. In addition, sleep disturbances caused by menopause symptoms may contribute to brain fog.

Chronic heavy drinking

Excessive alcohol intake is toxic to brain cells. Chronic alcohol abuse leads to memory loss. Over time, alcohol abuse may also increase the risk of dementia. Because of the damaging effects of excessive drinking, experts advise limiting one's daily intake to one or two drinks.

Hypothyroidism

In hypothyroidism, a condition in which the thyroid gland doesn't produce enough thyroid hormone, a person may develop problems with concentration and memory. If physical symptoms such as unexplained weight gain or hair loss accompany the memory difficulties, a physician should be consulted.

Vitamin B12 deficiency

This vitamin is known for protecting neurons and contributing to general brain health. As we age, the brain is less able to absorb nutrients such as B12, which may result in a deficiency. Smoking and drinking may increase this effect. A physician can diagnose whether there is a deficiency and prescribe appropriate treatment.

Hydrocephalus

Normal Pressure Hydrocephalus (NPH) is an excessive accumulation of cerebrospinal fluid (CSF) in the brain that typically occurs in individuals 60 years of age and older. It is characterized by the gradual onset of a triad of symptoms, usually starting with difficulty walking that mimics Parkinson's disease (small, shuffling steps and an increase in falls), urinary incontinence, and mild dementia in the form of forgetfulness, short-term memory loss, loss of interest in activities, or mood changes. However, successful treatment of NPH often allows an individual to return to an active lifestyle without memory difficulties. (The urinary incontinence is the significant difference between NPH and Parkinson's.)

Sleep apnea or other sleep problems

Sleep-disordered breathing is an umbrella term for a group of conditions that cause breathing abnormalities while a person is sleeping. Obstructive sleep apnea (OSA) is the most common type in which muscles in the back of the throat relax too much, narrowing or completely blocking the airway and interrupting airflow. These episodes, though only 10 to 30 seconds, briefly deprive the brain of oxygen. The consequences include loud snoring and hypoxia (low oxygen levels in the bloodstream). The latter triggers the brain to wake up the body briefly and breathe, but this cycle recurs numerous times throughout the night, depriving one of needed sleep.

A study in the journal *Neurology* found that sleep apnea may hasten the rate of cognitive decline in older adults (Osorio et al., 2015). Researchers reviewed the medical histories of 2,470 people, ages 55 to 90, who were participating in the Alzheimer's Disease Neuroimaging Initiative. At the study's start, participants had no memory or thinking problems, early-stage mild cognitive impairment, or probable Alzheimer's disease. Those with sleep-disordered breathing were diagnosed with mild cognitive impairment 10 years earlier, on average, than those without sleep-breathing problems. When the researchers looked solely at people who developed mild cognitive impairment during the study, they found that those with untreated sleep-disordered breathing showed signs of cognitive deterioration at an average age of 77, compared with age 90 for those without difficulty breathing while asleep. The onset of Alzheimer's also occurred at a younger age (83) in those with sleep-disordered breathing than in participants without sleep troubles (88).

A research study that combined data from 14 studies involving more than four million adults found that people with sleep-disordered breathing were 26 percent more likely to experience cognitive decline than those without the condition. They also performed somewhat worse in executive function (higher-level cognitive skills which control and coordinate other cognitive abilities and behaviors). The findings implied that sleep-disordered breathing may be an important modifiable risk factor for dementia and other cognitive impairment (Leng, et al., 2017). Neither this nor other studies cited proves that sleep-disordered breathing causes cognitive decline, but they do provide evidence that it may worsen the problem or hasten its onset.

Risk Factors for Alzheimer's Disease

The major risk factors for developing Alzheimer's disease can be divided into *modifiable* and *nonmodifiable*. In other words, there are some risk factors over which we have no control, but there are many which we can influence by our lifestyle choices.

Non-Modifiable Risk Factors

Genetics

A minority of cases of Alzheimer's disease (less than five percent) are inherited or "familial," due to changes or alterations in specific genes directly passed on from parent to child. If a person has familial Alzheimer's disease, each of his/her children has a higher risk of inheriting the disease-causing gene and developing dementia. Three familial Alzheimer's disease risk genes have been discovered so far: the PS1, PS2, and APP genes. If one has an alteration in any one of these genes, he/she will have a greater chance of developing young (early) onset familial Alzheimer's disease. Possession of one or more copies of the epsilon 4 variant of the apolipoprotein E gene (APOE4) is also associated with increased risk.

Age

Alzheimer's disease is not a normal part of aging, but the strongest known risk factor for AD is increasing age. After age 65, the risk of developing AD doubles approximately every five years.

Modifiable Risk Factors

Smoking

According to the World Health Organization, cigarette smoking is associated with an increased risk of dementia and Alzheimer's. Researchers believe this has to do with the vessels that carry blood around our body and to our brains. There is strong evidence that smokers are at a 45% higher risk of developing Alzheimer's disease than non-smokers or ex-smokers. They are also at a somewhat higher risk of developing vascular or other forms of dementia. Quitting smoking may lessen the risk of dementia.

Hearing Loss and Cognitive Decline

NIA-funded research has indicated that hearing loss may impact cognition and dementia risk in older adults. A 2011 study found that older adults with hearing loss were more likely to develop dementia than those with normal hearing. In fact, there was a relationship between level of uncorrected hearing loss and level of dementia risk: mild hearing loss was associated with a two-fold increase in risk; moderate hearing loss with a three-fold increase in risk, and severe hearing loss with a five-fold increase in risk (Lin et al., 2011).

A more recent study found that cognitive abilities (including memory and concentration) declined faster in older adults with hearing loss than in those with normal hearing (Lin et al., 2013). These observations raise the question of whether correcting hearing loss might slow or stop cognitive decline and/or dementia onset.

A study that followed nearly 3,700 adults age 65 and older for 25 years found no direct effect of hearing loss on cognitive decline (Amieva et al, 2015). What they did find was that hearing loss causes depression and social isolation, which then affect brain health. They noted that if people with hearing loss use hearing aids, they would be more likely to engage in social interactions and participate in cognitively stimulating activities, which could slow cognitive decline.

In any event, hearing loss detracts from cognitive processing of verbal information. It is also difficult to be accurate about information not clearly processed (in other words, if you didn't hear it, you can't remember it). When people are unable to hear conversations, they tend to withdraw socially, and socialization is extremely important for brain health (see Chapter Three). The takeaway is that, if possible, one should do what one can to strengthen one's ability to hear.

High Blood Pressure

Since high blood pressure affects the heart, arteries, and blood circulation, it increases the risk of developing Alzheimer's disease and vascular dementia. Research has shown that abnormal blood pressure in both mid- and late life is associated with dementia risk; the evidence supports recommending blood pressure management to reduce risk of cognitive decline and dementia (Arvanitakis, 2018). Lowering blood pressure through exercise, better diet, and possibly medications (if prescribed by a physician) can reduce the risk of heart disease and stroke, which are also risk factors for memory loss.

Diabetes

Research has shown that type 2 diabetes in midlife is associated with increased risk of dementia, Alzheimer's disease, vascular dementia and cognitive impairment. People who have type 2 diabetes are, on average, twice as likely to develop dementia compared to those without it. Diabetes tends to increase risk for heart attacks and strokes due to the cardiovascular problems it creates and the way it impairs blood vessels. People with diabetes end up with too much glucose in their blood which, over time, can lead to increased fatty deposits or clots on the insides of the blood vessel walls. These clots can narrow or block the blood vessels in the brain or neck, cutting off the blood supply, which stops the oxygen from getting to the brain and causes a stroke (www.stroke.org).

> *There is a fountain of youth: it is your mind, your talents, the creativity you bring to your life and the lives of people you love.*
> Sophia Loren

High Cholesterol

High total cholesterol levels in midlife increase the risk for developing dementia. High cholesterol is also a risk factor for hypertension and diabetes and contributes independently to cardiovascular risk. Research has shown that people who have their high cholesterol treated with drugs called "statins" have a lower risk of dementia.

Obesity and Lack of Physical Activity

Obesity and lack of physical activity are risk factors for diabetes and high blood pressure and may increase the risk of dementia and Alzheimer's disease.

Alcohol

People who drink moderate amounts of alcohol appear to have the lowest risk of developing dementia. Those who don't drink any alcohol at all may have a slightly higher risk, and those who drink excessively have the highest risk. Schwarzinger and colleagues (2018), who did a nationwide study, found an association between alcohol use disorders and all types of dementia, even after controlling for potential confounding risk factors. They suggested that, to promote cognitive health, older adults should be screened for heavy drinking at physician visits and offered treatment if needed.

Head Injuries

People who experience severe or repeated head injuries, such as boxers, football players and combat veterans, are at higher risk of dementia, cognitive impairment and neurodegenerative disease than those who experience no head injury. The Alzheimer's Association recommends using helmets (for motorcycle or bicycle riding, skiing, etc.), wearing seat belts, and "fall-proofing" your home to decrease your chances of getting a serious brain injury. Fall-proofing is particularly important for older adults on blood thinners, as a blow to the head could result in bleeding within the brain that could be fatal or resemble a serious stroke. (Note that concussions without loss of consciousness wherein you recall the incident are "mild," not "severe." Initial cognitive difficulties typically resolve within three months and are unlikely to lead to dementia.)

Cognitive and Social Engagement

As stated earlier, much research suggests that remaining mentally and socially active may support brain health and possibly reduce the risk of Alzheimer's and other dementias. Social and cognitive engagement contribute to *cognitive reserve*, resulting in a more enriched brain which may be able to better withstand the onslaught of disease. This enrichment enables the brain to compensate during early Alzheimer's by using alternate routes of neuron-to-neuron communication to complete a cognitive task.

Chapter Three
Brain SENSE: Lifestyle Practices for Brain Health

Review of Chapter Two

1. What is the primary difference between Mild Cognitive Impairment (MCI) and dementia? (p. 9)
2. Explain the relationship between Alzheimer's disease and dementia. (p. 11)
3. What are some potentially *treatable* causes of memory difficulty? (p. 14)

In this chapter you will learn how your lifestyle choices make a difference in your brain's health and function. When I was young, I recall hearing about people hoping to find a so-called "fountain of youth," and I truly did not comprehend the *what* or *why* of it. Once I turned 60, I understood completely why one would desire to find a way to maintain youthfulness, especially in appearance and mobility. Current research focuses on what people need to do to maintain cognitive function in the face of aging. As the brain controls everything we do, efforts to keep it functioning at an optimum level—while not providing a "fountain of youth"—can certainly enhance our quality of life and relationships.

The 2016 AARP Member Opinion Survey, to which approximately 23,000 AARP members responded, found that 90% are "extremely/very interested" in staying mentally sharp (Hagerty, 2016). Though heredity does influence what happens to the brain as we age, lifestyle plays a more prominent role in determining brain health. What we eat and drink, how active we are, whether we smoke, the degree of education we have obtained, our spirituality, the amount of time we spend sleeping, and the amount of time we spend interacting with others, have all been found to relate in some way to brain health. Research is identifying activities and behaviors which appear to slow cognitive decline and possibly delay the onset of diseases like Alzheimer's.

Multiple studies support the idea that health education and lifestyle interventions can reduce the incidence of dementia. The Finnish Geriatric Intervention Study to Prevent Cognitive Impairment and Disability (FINGER) enrolled 1,260 Finnish people aged 60 to 77 who scored high on dementia risk factors, including hypertension, high cholesterol, and obesity (Ngandu et al., 2015). Participants were randomly assigned to either a 2-year multidomain intervention (diet, exercise, cognitive training, vascular risk monitoring) or to a control group (general health advice). The primary outcome was change in cognition as measured through a comprehensive neuropsychological test battery (NTB), evaluating multiple aspects of cognitive function. The intervention group scored about 25 percent higher than the control group on global cognition, and about 40 percent higher on memory tests. Performance on tests of executive function and processing speed was about twice as good as for controls. Cognitive decline over the course of the study was 30 percent more likely in the control group than in the treatment group.

The FINGER study showed that a multidomain approach is feasible in real-world settings, since most people completed the trial. Participants came to 90 percent of their scheduled sessions with health coaches and reported enjoying them. Data on the intervention group showed that they exercised more and ate more fish and vegetables than controls, demonstrating that they did change their behavior, at least in the short term. They scored higher in measures of mobility, ability to perform daily activities, and quality of life. The only adverse event reported was sore muscles from exercise. The results of the FINGER 2-year study suggest that a multidomain intervention could improve or maintain cognitive functioning in at-risk older adults.

Research continues to show that memory loss and cognitive decline are not an inevitable part of aging. In a manner similar to the way muscles grow stronger with exercise, the brain also grows if it is engaged in the right activities. These discoveries have fueled the rapid growth of the brain fitness movement, some of which takes the form of brain training software and websites, such as Lumosity, Cognifit, Brain HQ by PositScience, and others. Books with puzzles, brain teasers, Sudoku, and other brain "challenges" also proliferate. According to SharpBrains, a leading market research firm, the digital brain health market will grow to six billion dollars by 2020.

> *I don't want to achieve immortality through my work,*
> *I want to achieve it by not dying.*
> Woody Allen

In recent years there has been an abundance of research studies looking at the impact of various lifestyle practices on brain health. I devised the acronym Brain *SENSE* to make it easier to remember the most important lifestyle practices identified by this research.

Brain SENSE: Lifestyle Practices for Optimum Brain Health

S = socialization

E = exercise

N = nutrition

S = sleep, spirituality

E = education

S = Socialization

Studies have repeatedly found that socialization improves cognitive health, while social disengagement is a risk factor for cognitive impairment. Research shows that older adults who maintain a meaningful role in their lives and are more socially engaged experience less cognitive decline (Krueger et al., 2009; Ristau, 2011). By remaining integrated and involved through hobbies, clubs, ministry or volunteering, you can maintain a sense of purpose. The important thing is to interact with other people. According to a recent report by The Lancet Commission, 2.3% of dementia cases could be prevented simply by reducing social isolation. Staying engaged in family networks and friendships is crucial as we age, especially for people who are retired and no longer go to a job each day, and for those who live alone.

Bryan James, at Rush Alzheimer's Disease Center in Chicago, uses the term "life space" to refer to the extent to which we move through various environments in our daily lives: from home to garden to restaurants to workplace and beyond. In a recent study, he and his colleagues found that seniors who had a constricted life space were almost twice as likely to develop Alzheimer's disease as seniors whose life space extended well beyond the home (James et al., 2011).

> *Being a part of a social network of friends and family*
> *is one of the most dependable predictors of longevity.*
> Rowe and Kahn

Social activity supports cognitive health by promoting:
- complex interpersonal exchanges, enhancing or maintaining efficient neural networks
- meaningful social roles and a sense of purpose, resulting in a reduction of the stress response
- regular exercise/walking, leading to vascular changes in the brain and cerebral oxygenation that might protect against neuropathology

Research on SuperAgers also suggests the importance of social relationships for maintaining cognitive function. SuperAgers are adults over age 80 whose performance on tests of episodic memory (conscious recollection of information or previous experiences) is at least as good as that of people 20 to 30 years younger. They are being studied by researchers at the Northwestern University SuperAging Program, Massachusetts General Hospital, and Harvard Medical School. Neuroimaging findings also suggest that the brains of these SuperAgers may be physiologically different than those of us who do not fall into that category (Sun, 2016).

Recent SuperAgers findings from Dr. Emily Rogalski and colleagues at Northwestern University add more evidence on the importance of positive social relationships (Maher, 2017). To measure the effect of psychological well-being on SuperAgers and age-matched controls, Rogalski's team administered memory tests and a psychological status questionnaire. While both groups reported similarly high levels of psychological well-being, SuperAgers scored significantly higher on the positive social relationships scale, indicating they enjoyed satisfying, high-quality relationships. These data add to a growing literature about the importance of social engagement and positive social connections as we age.

E = Exercise

> **NOTE:** Suggestions presented in this book regarding exercise and nutrition should not be followed without conferring with one's physician or a medical professional.

John Ratey of Harvard asserted in his book *Spark: The Revolutionary New Science of Exercise and the Brain* (2008) that exercise is the single best thing you can do for your brain. Every time your heart beats, 25% of the blood it generates goes directly to your brain. That blood carries oxygen and nutrients vital to brain health. The more fit your heart, the more effectively it can feed your brain with what it needs to stay sharp.

As we age, brain cells wear down, communication between neurons decreases, and certain parts of the brain shrink. The capillaries which bring nutrients and oxygen to the brain narrow, restricting blood flow. Exercise fosters connections between neurons and encourages neurogenesis (the birth of new brain cells). In older adults, exercise promotes the production of *dopamine*, a critical neurotransmitter which, when it diminishes with age, can contribute to apathy, depression, and/or a lack of motivation.

Brain-derived neurotrophic factor (BDNF) is an essential ingredient for neurogenesis in the hippocampus. When neurons are created there, BDNF helps them to stay viable and grow. It also helps neurons in the frontal lobes heal and repair to remain healthy (Fotuhi, 2013). Although these neurotrophic factors diminish with age, research provides evidence that exercise elevates the supply of BDNF for neuroplasticity and neurogenesis. Thus, BDNF can be thought of as a fertilizer for the brain, which is probably why John Ratey has dubbed it, "MiracleGro for the brain" (Ratey, 2008).

The hippocampus is a curved structure deep inside the medial temporal lobe of the brain vital to certain types of memory. Researchers have found that older adults who are more physically fit tend to have bigger hippocampi and better spatial memory than their couch potato contemporaries (Erickson et al., 2009). This study showed that hippocampus size in physically fit adults accounts for about 40 percent of their spatial memory advantage.

Studies have also found that the hippocampus shrinks with age, a process coinciding with small but significant cognitive declines. The rate at which this occurs differs among individuals. Researchers at the University of Illinois and the University of Pittsburgh measured the cardiorespiratory fitness of 165 adults (109 of them female) between 59 and 81 years of age (Kramer & Erickson, 2007). Using magnetic resonance imaging (MRI), the researchers measured the volume of the subjects' left and right hippocampi. They tested the participants' spatial reasoning and found a significant association between an individual's fitness and his or her performance on certain spatial memory tests. They also found a strong correlation between fitness and hippocampus size. The people who were more fit had a bigger hippocampus and better spatial memory.

One study (Firth et al., 2018) used statistical analysis to extract the overall findings from 14 separate clinical trials examining the effects of aerobic exercise on hippocampal volume across 737 participants. Although there was no significant effect from aerobic exercise on total hippocampal volume, there was evidence that exercise prevented the left hippocampus from shrinking as much. Thus, the authors concluded that aerobic exercise may prevent age-related hippocampal deterioration and maintain neuronal health.

"This is really a clinically significant finding because it supports the notion that your lifestyle choices and behaviors may influence brain shrinkage in old age," said Erickson. Staying fit may help maintain the brain regions involved in learning and memory. The influence on spatial memory is particularly important because older adults with that difficulty often end up losing their independence. In other words, their driving privileges are revoked, or they don't leave the house for fear of getting lost.

In a study published in the *Journals of Gerontology*, Dr. Stanley Colcombe (Colcombe et al., 2006) found that increasing blood flow to the brain can trigger neurochemical changes that increase the production of new brain cells and decrease the risk of dementia. In this study, as little as three hours a week of brisk walking (aerobic exercise) resulted in the participants aged 60 to 90 performing better on complex tasks, focusing, and ignoring irrelevant information.

Other research has shown that regular aerobic exercise boosts intellectual performance and lowers risk for dementia—by up to 38 percent in some studies. Walking at a vigorous pace at least 30 minutes a day, five or six days a week is reported to be beneficial. *If* your physician approves, a cardiovascular workout for 30 minutes at least four times a week in your target heart rate zone would be even better.

The cognitive benefits of physical fitness through cardiovascular and strength training have been demonstrated in all types of studies (cross-sectional, longitudinal, and intervention) constituting one of the most reliable messages about successful aging (Kramer & Erickson, 2007; Hertzog et al., 2008; Lustig et al., 2009). A randomized clinical trial with sedentary men and women found that a six-month program of aerobic exercise resulted in significant improvements in executive functioning (including language/verbal fluency and memory) in older adults with cardiovascular disease risk factors, subjective cognitive complaints, and cognitive impairment without dementia (Blumenthal et al., 2018).

Exercise is considered by many to be *the* most important anti-aging medicine known; it is believed to be a tool that can prevent or postpone Alzheimer's and other age-related diseases. A natural antioxidant, exercise lowers cholesterol, blood sugar and insulin levels. It helps keep the heart healthy, reduces brain inflammation, and turns on neural enzymes that clear amyloid plaque. Exercise can also improve sleep, which is often disrupted by stress, depression and/or anxiety. People benefit by scheduling time daily for exercise, whether in the form of walking, running, biking, swimming, dancing, or whatever type of movement motivates them. Recommended amounts of exercise are a minimum of 8,000 to 10,000 steps daily; however, a recent study at UCLA found that even 4,000 or more steps per day improved cognitive functioning in a group of 72-year olds (Siddarth et al., 2018). Stretching/strengthening or aerobic exercise three to five times a week or more is also beneficial. Gardening, dancing, playing Wii sports, or doing "Sit and Be Fit" exercises can also provide physical activity. If possible, avoid being sedentary.

Exercise can help counteract the effects of cortisol, a hormone whose levels increase with stress. Cortisol has been shown to negatively affect memory and learning in older adults. To combat cortisol, physical activity can increase the brain's production of endorphins, the relaxing "feel-good" neurotransmitters (sometimes referred to as "runner's high").

Laughter and humor are also vehicles for relieving stress. Dr. Gurinder Bains (Bains et al., 2014) studied short-term memory in older adults (average age 68); half watched a 20-minute funny video and the other half just sat in the waiting room. The humor group had a significant increase in learning ability, delayed recall, and decreased cortisol levels, as compared with the control group.

The life of Olga Kotelko has been featured in a book entitled *What Makes Olga Run?* by Bruce Grierson. This woman, who died in 2014, was a track star in her nineties. She didn't begin her track-and-field career until age 77. Between 1996 and 2014—the year she turned 95—she earned 37 world records in 100m, 200m, high jump, long jump, javelin, discus, hammer, and shot put. She believed her good health and high energy could be attributed to maintaining a positive attitude, saying, "Wishing for something won't make it happen; you have to work for it" (www.Elmag.com/olgaruns). Olga developed nine rules for living, the first of which was to "keep moving." She knew the importance of not being sedentary. She also advocated setting goals, not complaining, only doing what you enjoy (especially regarding exercise) and starting now!

> *Never give up. You are never too old to chase a dream. Don't be afraid.*
> Olga Kotelko

N = Nutrition

One can easily find supplements, candy bars, and other edible products which claim to enhance brain function. The problem is that there is little scientific evidence to back the claims their manufacturers make about what they can do for the brain. A Consumer Reports article in the *Washington Post* cited a 2017 Government Accountability Office report which analyzed hundreds of ads promoting memory-enhancing supplements online. The report identified 27 making what seemed to be illegal claims about treating or preventing diseases such as dementia. Supplements are loosely regulated, and some may even contain undisclosed ingredients or prescription drugs. Many interact (sometimes dangerously) with medications. "Don't be misled by hype," says Marvin M. Lipman, Consumer Reports' chief medical adviser. "They are not only a waste of money, but some can also be harmful" (Calderone, 2018).

The brain needs nutrients to build and maintain structure, function well, and protect itself from diseases and premature aging (Turner, 2011). The brain uses about 20 to 30 percent of a person's energy intake at rest, and higher amounts during activities such as problem solving. Establishing and maintaining healthy eating habits can help prevent age-related cognitive decline.

Healthy brain eating includes:
- Eliminating trans fats (hydrogenated foods, like chips and fries)
- Eating antioxidants: 5 half-cup servings daily of fruits and vegetables
- Eating more Omega-3 unsaturated fatty acids (fatty fish like salmon; nuts, seeds)
- Staying hydrated (alcohol and caffeine can have a dehydrating effect)

An informative website for healthy eating is:
www.alz.org/alzheimers-dementia/facts-figures

Mediterranean Diet

The Mediterranean Diet is characterized by abundant plant foods in the form of fruits, vegetables, breads, other forms of cereals, potatoes, beans, nuts and seeds; fresh fruit as the typical dessert; olive oil as the main source of monounsaturated fat; dairy products as principally cheese and yogurt; a low to moderate consumption of fish and poultry; fewer than four eggs per week; and red meat and wine consumed in low to moderate amounts, normally during meals. However, there are several definitions of the Mediterranean diet, because dietary habits vary considerably across the countries bordering the Mediterranean Sea (Feart et al., 2010).

A growing body of evidence suggests that adherence to the Mediterranean diet (MD) may protect against cognitive decline and dementia (Petersson & Philippou,

2016). In a systematic review of 32 studies, the majority showed that the MD was associated with improved cognitive function, a decreased risk of cognitive impairment or decreased risk of dementia or AD. Although these findings from epidemiologic studies provide evidence for a correlation between the MD and cognition, they do not necessarily prove a cause-and-effect relationship. Two prospective studies involving cohorts of Americans and French individuals aged 65 years and older also found that a high adherence to the Mediterranean diet was associated with slower cognitive decline, reduced risk of mild cognitive impairment conversion to Alzheimer's disease, and reduced risk of Alzheimer's disease (Feart et al., 2010). A Mediterranean-style diet pattern most likely does not *fully* explain the better health of persons who adhere to it, as the diet may be only one of a complex set of favorable social and lifestyle factors that contribute to better global health.

MIND Diet

MIND stands for "Mediterranean-DASH Intervention for Neurodegenerative Delay." This diet combines aspects of the Mediterranean diet and the Dietary Approaches to Stop Hypertension (DASH) diet, with the goal of creating an eating approach that can reduce the risk of dementia and the decline in brain health that often accompanies aging. There are no specific guidelines for following the MIND diet; rather the focus is on eating more of the 10 recommended food groups, and less of the five food groups the diet recommends you limit.

Recommended foods:

- Six or more servings per week of green, leafy vegetables, including kale, spinach, cooked greens and salads
- All other vegetables, especially non-starchy vegetables with more nutrients but fewer calories, at least once a day
- Berries high in antioxidants, including strawberries, blueberries, raspberries and blackberries, at least twice per week
- Five or more servings of nuts per week
- Olive oil for cooking
- At least three servings per day of whole grains, preferably oatmeal, quinoa, brown rice, whole-wheat pasta and 100% whole-wheat bread
- Fish – at least once per week, preferably fatty fish like salmon, sardines, trout, tuna and mackerel for their high amounts of omega-3 fatty acids
- Beans – in at least four meals per week, including lentils and soybeans
- Poultry – chicken (not fried) or turkey at least twice a week
- Wine – one glass daily, either red or white; research has suggested that the red wine compound resveratrol may help protect against Alzheimer's disease

Foods to consume in limited quantities:
- Butter and margarine – less than one tablespoon per day, substituting olive oil as the primary cooking fat
- Cheese – less than once per week
- Red meat – no more than three servings per week of beef, pork, lamb and products made from these meats
- Fried food – less than once per week, especially from fast-food restaurants
- Pastries and sweets – four or fewer times per week, including processed junk food and desserts such as ice cream, cookies, brownies, snack cakes, donuts, and candy

The scientists who created the MIND diet think it may work by reducing oxidative stress and inflammation, which together can harm the brain. Research has shown that following the MIND diet even a moderate amount is associated with a reduced risk of Alzheimer's disease (Morris et al., 2015a). According to this research, eating more of the 10 recommended foods and less of the foods to avoid has been associated with a lower risk of Alzheimer's disease, and better brain function over time (Morris et al., 2015b).

"In a perfect world, food should provide all the necessary nutrients to support optimal brain health" (Turner, 2011, p. 104). The reality is that this is not a perfect world, and so some people will need to include in their diet supplements of individual vitamins, minerals, and other nutrients, *if* their physician approves. An essential protection against age-related cognitive decline is to establish and maintain healthy eating habits. Nutritional advocates often tell people to "eat the rainbow," which is a simple way of reminding people that a variety of fruits and vegetables in the diet will provide vitamins, minerals, and antioxidants that the body needs.

> *Few minds wear out; more rust out.*
> Christian Nestell Bovee

As we age, the brain experiences more and more oxidative stress, often referred to as *rusting*, one of the major causes of all disease. One way to control rusting is through the intake of *antioxidants* which are found in abundance in colorful fruits and vegetables – the dark purples of blueberries, the deep reds of pomegranates, the rich green of kale and spinach, the bright orange of sweet potatoes. A study in the *Journal of the American Medical Association* (Beydoun, 2015) described associations of dietary antioxidants with cognitive function in a large biracial population and reported that people who ate more dietary antioxidants had 70% less Alzheimer's and dementia. The researchers concluded that dietary antioxidants can inhibit reactions leading to neurodegeneration and thus prevent or delay cognitive impairment. A guideline is to eat eight to 10 servings (half cups) of these colorful fruits and vegetables per day to protect the brain.

A recent report in the journal *Neurology* found that a diet containing approximately one serving of green leafy vegetables per day is associated with slower age-related cognitive decline (Morris et al., 2017). Dr. Martha Clare Morris and colleagues from Rush University in Chicago and the Tufts Human Nutrition Research Center in Boston followed 960 older adults enrolled in the Rush Memory and Aging Project. The research team focused on the consumption level of green leafy vegetables like spinach, kale, collards, and lettuce, most of which are rich in brain-healthy nutrients like vitamin K, lutein, folate, and beta carotene. Previous research (Kang, 2005; Morris, 2006) suggested these leafy greens have protective factors against cognitive decline, so the study looked at the association between consumption of them and performance on cognitive tests.

Dementia-free participants averaging 81 years of age underwent annual tests assessing cognition (episodic memory, working memory, semantic memory, visuospatial ability, and perceptual speed) over five years. Food frequency questionnaires were used to assess how frequently people ate some 144 items over the previous 12 months. Results of this study indicate that consumption of green leafy vegetables is associated with a slower rate of cognitive decline in older adults, possibly due to the neuroprotective actions of specific nutrients. The researchers suggest that adding a daily serving of green leafy vegetables to one's diet may contribute to brain health (Morris, et al., 2017).

Omegas

Decline in *fluid intelligence*, one of the most debilitating aspects of cognitive aging, has been linked to omega-3 polyunsaturated fatty acid (ω-3 PUFA) status. Fluid intelligence refers to the capacity to reason and solve novel problems, independent of any knowledge from the past. Research on the influence of ω-3 PUFA on brain aging has grown exponentially during the last decade. Two intervention studies obtained clear evidence that ω-3 PUFA was involved in neurotransmission, neuroprotection, and neurogenesis, thereby helping the brain cope with aging. These recent studies support and clarify how ω-3 PUFA protects against age-related brain damage (Denis, 2015). Other research suggests that in addition to eating fish and fish oil to get neuroprotective effects, the fats from nuts, seeds and oils can also make a difference in the brain (Zamroziewicz et al., 2017).

Some of the best fish to eat for omega-3s are mackerel, salmon, and seabass. Flaxseeds, chia seeds, walnuts, and soybeans are also good sources.

Caffeine

Caffeine has both good and bad effects on the brain. It can increase alertness, boost concentration, and improve mood. However, it can also disturb sleep in some people, especially if consumed too close to bedtime. A recent study reported that coffee/caffeine consumption is not harmful if consumed at levels of 200 mg in one sitting (around 2½ cups of coffee) or 400 mg daily (around 5 cups of coffee). Lifelong coffee/caffeine consumption has been associated with prevention of cognitive decline, and with reduced risk of developing stroke, Parkinson's disease and Alzheimer's disease (Nehlig, 2016). That author states that daily caffeine consumption can be part of a healthy balanced diet even for older adults.

Relationship of Smoking and Alcohol to Alzheimer's and Dementia

Smoking and heavy drinking are two of the most preventable risk factors for Alzheimer's disease. Not only does smoking increase the odds by nearly 79 percent for those over 65, but researchers at Miami's Mt. Sinai Medical Center warn that a combination of these two behaviors reduces the age of Alzheimer's onset by six to seven years. When you stop smoking, the brain benefits almost immediately from improved circulation, no matter your age. However, brain changes from alcohol abuse can only be reversed in their early stages.

How the body handles alcohol changes with age, and the same amount of alcohol may affect an older person differently than when he or she was younger. Some older adults can feel "high" without increasing the amount of alcohol they drink, and that experience can increase their likelihood of having balance problems, car accidents, and falls. Older women are generally more sensitive than men to the effects of alcohol. According to Dr. Anthony Komaroff of Harvard Medical School there are two main biological explanations. The first involves an enzyme, alcohol dehydrogenase (ADH), which breaks down alcohol in the stomach and the liver. Women have considerably less ADH in their stomach linings than men, so more alcohol leaves their stomach and is absorbed into their blood. As a result, one drink for a woman has about twice the effect as one for a man. Second, pound for pound, . a woman's body contains less water and more fatty tissue than a man's. Water dilutes alcohol in the blood; fat retains it. So, alcohol remains at higher concentrations for longer periods of time in a woman's body and exposes her brain to more alcohol.

For some older adults, drinking excessive alcohol can cause them to be forgetful and confused, symptoms which could be mistaken for signs of Alzheimer's disease or dementia. A recent study of mice which appeared in the journal *Scientific Reports* showed that low levels of alcohol consumption tamp down inflammation and help the brain clear away toxins, including those associated with Alzheimer's disease (Lundgaard, 2018). This may help explain why previous studies have shown that low-to-moderate alcohol intake is associated with a lesser risk of dementia, while heavy drinking for many years increases the risk of cognitive decline.

In excess, alcohol works as a neurotoxin, meaning that it kills neurons and impairs neurogenesis—the birth of new neurons—in the hippocampus, a region critical to creating new memories. Prolonged alcohol abuse results in a condition called *alcohol-induced dementia*. Moderate alcohol intake increases neurogenesis and may help counteract oxidative stress in neurons. Some evidence that wine is more strongly neuroprotective than other forms of alcohol suggests that the *resveratrol* found in red wine and red grape skin may also play a role because it has significant antioxidant properties.

Hydration

Older adults are an at-risk population for dehydration, partially because they tend to have decreased perception of thirst, and partially because total body water as a percentage of total body weight decreases progressively with increasing age. In addition, some older adults rely on others for access to water. A study of the effects of mild dehydration on cognitive performance in older adults living in retirement communities, which controlled for cognitive effects from blood pressure, age, and education, found that poorer hydration was statistically associated with decreased memory and slowing of psychomotor speed. In the older women, a significant relationship existed between mild dehydration and cognitive functions. Better hydration correlated with better performance on tests of memory. Dehydrated older adults tend to exhibit higher levels of fatigue and are less clear-minded (Pross, 2017). Other research shows that dehydration actually makes brain tissues shrink and may contribute to age-related cognitive deterioration (Lauriola et al., 2018; Sfera, et al., 2016; Thornton, 2014).

S = Sleep and Spirituality

Sleep

How many hours of sleep do you get per night? Most adults require seven or eight hours. Some indicators that you are getting enough sleep are that you feel well rested when you wake up, and perhaps wake up without an alarm. Other signs include not feeling a need for a caffeine boost and skin that is clear and glowing. According to the CDC, 28% of adults reported getting an average of six hours of sleep or less per day. One study reported that 71% of Americans sleep with a cell phone next to their bed. The blue light emitted acts as a stimulant interfering with the natural wake/sleep cycle. We have too many devices in our homes, often in our bedrooms, that emit beeps and other sounds, glow and intermittently light up, or vibrate, all of which can disturb sleep.

According to a poll by the National Sleep Foundation, nearly a third of adults complain that daytime sleepiness interferes with their lives. In her book, *The Sleep Revolution* (2016), Arianna Huffington addresses the trend to sacrifice sleep in order to complete our to-do list. She cites scientific findings associating sleep deprivation with increased risk for diabetes, heart attack, stroke, cancer, obesity, and Alzheimer's disease.

Sleep is vital for keeping us mentally sharp and alert. Neurocognitive functions, like short-term memory and high-level mental tasks that require paying attention to several things at once, are particularly vulnerable to sleep loss. Research shows that any degree of sleepiness will impair performance and mood, so getting too little sleep can undermine productivity, creativity, and effectiveness, and can lead to serious health consequences down the road. Sleep deficits are cumulative; if you lose a half night of sleep, your body carries the debt forward into the next day, and the next. Sleep plays an important role in learning, memory encoding, and cognition. Insufficient quantity or quality of sleep leads not only to short-term neurocognitive dysfunction but also to permanent changes to the central nervous system.

Research shows that during sleep, the brain consolidates information, so new learning and memory pathways are encoded. Much of this occurs during REM (rapid eye movement) sleep, the sleep phase in which humans seem to do most of their dreaming. During the night we generally experience four to six sleep cycles, each lasting about 90 minutes. Each sleep cycle has three stages of non-REM sleep, and one stage of REM sleep. The amount of time in REM sleep increases with each succeeding cycle. Thus, the last hour of sleep may be the most important, mainly because it is usually the last hour of REM sleep. Those who are well rested are better able to learn a task and more likely to remember what they learned. It also reviews information acquired during the day and consolidates memories. A study by Maas (2011) revealed that getting less than six-and-a-half to seven hours of sleep can negatively affect learning, problem-solving, and memory. It is possible that some of the cognitive decline that accompanies aging may in part result from chronically poor sleep.

> *You need to remember to sleep because you have to sleep to remember!*
> James B. Maas

Sleep problems have been linked to declining memory and executive function in older people. Analysis of sleep and cognitive data from 3,968 men and 4,821 women enrolled in the *English Longitudinal Study of Aging* (ELSA) examined the quality and quantity of sleep over the period of a month. The study revealed an association between both quality and duration of sleep and brain function which changes with age. In adults between 50 and 64 years of age, short sleep (less than 6 hours per night) and long sleep (more than 8 hours per night) were both associated with lower brain function scores. By contrast, in older adults (65-89 years) lower brain function scores were observed only in long sleepers. In the older adults there was a significant relationship between sleep quality and the observed scores. Results indicated that optimizing sleep may postpone the decline in brain function seen with age or may slow or prevent the rapid decline that leads to dementia. Non-pharmacological improvements in sleep may provide a cost-effective and more accessible public health intervention for delaying or slowing cognitive decline (Miller et al., 2014).

When we lose sleep, or don't sleep at regular times or for a long enough time, our brain hormones become imbalanced, leading to higher cortisol (a stress hormone), and lower growth hormone (a healing and repair hormone). Over time, the stress of sleep deprivation eats away at our brain function. Sleep deprivation also dampens mood, possibly by keeping the brain from replenishing neurotransmitters such as dopamine. Sleep deprivation can also affect appetite and the body's use of glucose. Since our metabolic system is also partly regulated by sleep, this could lead to insulin resistance. The Sleep Heart Health Study (SHHS), which involved more than 1,400 people aged 53 to 93 years, found that sleep duration of either six hours or less or nine hours or more was associated with increased prevalence of diabetes or glucose intolerance, compared with seven to eight hours of sleep per night (Gottlieb et al., 2005). A Swedish study found a link between self-reported lack of sleep, low vitality and impaired glucose metabolism. The researchers identified short sleep duration as a risk factor for developing type 2 diabetes (Andersson et al., 2013).

Almost every neurodegenerative disease—including Alzheimer's—is associated with the buildup of toxic proteins in the brain. Researchers speculate that it is the accumulation of these proteins that kills neurons and leads to dementia. While we sleep, the brain undergoes a drainage process to flush out harmful toxins. In a study using mice, funded by the National Institute of Neurological Disorders and Stroke (NINDS), researchers demonstrated that the space between brain cells may increase during sleep, allowing the brain to flush out toxins that build up during waking hours. So, if the brain cleanses itself of toxic molecules during sleep, that makes sleep even more essential to brain health.

Sleep is also affected by the brain's secretion of *melatonin* (the sleep hormone regulated by light exposure). The brain produces melatonin primarily at night; levels drop during daylight. However, this secretion may decrease with exposure to artificial light, especially the blue part of the spectrum emanating from televisions, florescent bulbs, clock LEDs, and computer screens. Short-wavelength blue light plays an important role in mood, energy level, and sleep quality. In the morning, sunlight contains high concentrations of this "blue" light. When your eyes are exposed to it directly (not through a window or while wearing sunglasses), the blue light halts production of the sleep-inducing hormone melatonin and makes you feel more alert.

In the afternoon, the sun's rays lose their blue light, which allows your body to produce melatonin and start making you sleepy. By evening, your brain does not expect any blue light exposure and is very sensitive to it. The problem this creates for sleep is that most of our favorite evening devices—laptops, tablets, televisions, and mobile phones—emit short-wavelength blue light. This exposure impairs melatonin production and interferes with ability to fall asleep as well as the quality of sleep once you do nod off. Avoid these devices after dinner (television is okay for most people as long as they sit far enough away from the set). If you must use one of these devices in the evening, you can limit your exposure with a filter (many smart phones have this option within their settings) or protective eye wear.

During the day, especially upon awakening, you should strive to let light into your brain to suppress melatonin secretion: turning on lights, opening curtains, and pulling up shades. In the evening, when you want more melatonin to help you fall asleep, try to wind down activity and go to bed at about the same time every night.

Avoid exposure to bright and fluorescent lights before bedtime, and cover lights being emitted by electrical devices in your bedroom, such as alarm clocks, DVDs, and phones. If you must get up during the night, use a flashlight or nightlight and avoid turning on any bright lights. Try to keep your bedroom as dark as possible; if you cannot, wear a sleep mask.

> *When we don't have enough sleep … we are more easily frustrated, less happy, short-tempered, less vital.*
> William C. Dement

Getting exercise daily can help you sleep at night. Physical activity tires you out, making your body want to sleep. In addition, exercise causes your body to release chemicals called endorphins, which reduce stress, increase relaxation, and can act as sedatives, making it easier to fall asleep, provided you do not engage in vigorous exercise too close to bedtime.

Sleep is also affected by caffeine (from coffee, tea, soft drinks, and even chocolate). Caffeine's half-life (time taken for the body to eliminate one-half of it) is approximately 5 to 6 hours, but varies from person to person, depending on age, body weight, pregnancy status, medication intake and liver health. This is especially important as caffeine metabolism slows as we age. Also, caffeine triggers the release of cortisol, the stress hormone, which can wreak further havoc upon sleep.

Sleep Apnea

One in 15 adults has moderate to severe obstructive sleep apnea (OSA), a disorder in which breathing is interrupted during sleep as many as 30 times per hour. People with OSA often report such problems as poor concentration, difficulty with memory, and stress. According to research published in the online *Journal of Sleep Research* (Macey, 2016), people with sleep apnea show significant changes in the levels of two important brain chemicals (neurotransmitters), glutamate and gamma-aminobutyric acid (GABA), in a brain region called the insula. These neurotransmitters integrate signals from higher brain regions to regulate emotion, thinking, and physical functions such as blood pressure and perspiration. The researchers found that people with sleep apnea had decreased levels of GABA and unusually high levels of glutamate. Differences in the levels of these two chemicals negatively impact the brain's functions. Researchers hope to determine whether treating OSA can return these brain chemicals to normal levels and are investigating whether mindfulness exercises can reduce glutamate levels by calming the brain.

An analysis combining data from 14 studies involving more than 4.2 million adults showed that people with sleep-disordered breathing were 26 percent more likely to experience cognitive decline than those without the condition (Leng et al., 2017). Their study also showed that executive function—the mental processes for activities such as planning, organizing, paying attention, and following instructions—was slightly worse in people with sleep-disordered breathing.

A study that reviewed the medical histories of 2,470 people ages 55 to 90 reported that heavy snoring and sleep apnea may be linked to memory and thinking decline at an earlier age (Osorio et al., 2015). The researchers found that people who had sleep breathing problems developed Alzheimer's disease five years earlier than those who did not have sleep breathing problems, at an average age of 83 versus 88. They also found that those who treated their sleep breathing problems with a continuous positive airway pressure (CPAP) machine were not diagnosed with MCI until about 10 years later than those whose problems were not treated, or at age 82 instead of age 72. More research is needed to determine whether treatment of sleep disordered breathing, including the use of CPAP, might reduce the risk of cognitive impairment.

Sleep disorders are common in older adults. Oxygen loss and sleep fragmentation resulting from OSA are a possible cause of harm to the brain. Because treatment of OSA can lead to improved cognitive function, it is important for physicians to treat this disorder if it is diagnosed in patients presenting with memory or cognitive complaints. If you snore, discuss it with your doctor.

Suggestions for Getting Better Sleep

What do Leonardo da Vinci, Albert Einstein and Thomas Edison have in common? All were known for taking naps! Companies like British Airways, Google, and Nike encourage their employees to take power naps, defined as a 15 to 20-minute siesta, which results in a winding down of activity in the brain's prefrontal cortex. The short duration of a power nap prevents a person's brain from entering slow-wave, deeper sleep. Sara Mednick, Ph.D., a scientist at the Salk Institute for Biological Studies who is at the forefront of napping research, says that a power nap gets the sleeper into and out of rejuvenate sleep as fast as possible (Mednick, 2006). Her research shows that power naps can lift productivity and mood, lower stress, and improve memory and learning. Mednick has found through fMRIs of nappers that brain activity stays high throughout the day with a nap; without one, it declines as the day wears on.

- Keep consistent times for going to bed and getting up.
- Get at least seven to eight hours of sleep per night.

- Make the bedroom dark and quiet, and wear socks to bed if it's cold.
- Determine your brain's tolerance for caffeine; if necessary, avoid consuming caffeinated beverages later in the day. This goes for chocolate as well. ☹
- Regular exercise can give you those endorphins that relax you and help you sleep. Exercise can also make you tired enough to sleep, but observe your personal reaction to vigorous exercise shortly before retiring.
- If you snore and/or suspect you may have sleep apnea, discuss this with your physician, who may order a sleep study.
- Focus on your breathing, inhaling deeply and exhaling slowly. If you can focus on just your breath, other thoughts will not enter your mind, allowing you to relax and hopefully fall asleep.
- Visualize being in a place of tranquility, such as an open meadow or a beach with waves gently lapping the shore. This can slow brain wave activity, helping you to fall asleep.
- Go through a progressive muscle relaxation routine. Tense and relax muscles throughout your body, beginning with your feet and working up to your head.
- Avoid anything that energizes or wakes you up too close to bedtime, including vigorous exercise, video games, or even suspenseful books.
- Get light early in the day; a study showed that people who got more environmental light because their office had access to windows also had better sleep quality and mood.
- If you have trouble falling asleep, start winding down from your day at least one or two hours before bedtime. Don't watch TV or check your email.
- Use aromatherapy with a lavender scent or take a hot bath with Epsom salt and 10 drops of lavender oil (lavender oil is known for promoting relaxation and a good night of sleep).

Spirituality

Regarding spirituality, a review of research by Koenig (2012) has found that prayer, meditation, and relaxation practices are associated with:

- Improvement in psychological well-being
- Reduced levels of depression
- Reduction in disease
- Increase in life span
- Enhanced immune system

Attending a formal place of worship relates to better quality of life and longevity. Meditation and relaxation techniques are good methods to help you slow down and turn inward for balance and stability.

E = Education / Cognitive Stimulation (Use Your Head!)

> *When you stop learning, your brain starts dying.*
> Dr. Daniel Amen

Education, or cognitive stimulation, involves exposing the brain to novel and complex challenges, or even just learning something new. Participation in cognitively stimulating activities is an effective way to develop a stronger, healthier brain through building the "cognitive reserve" associated with slower late-life cognitive decline. A brain with a strong reserve has formed many cellular connections and is rich in brain cell density. This reserve protects the brain against the onset of mental deterioration, such as Alzheimer's Disease (AD), because the abundance and redundancy of neurons enables it to function relatively normally for a longer period after neurodegenerative diseases begin attacking it.

K. Warner Schaie's life's work, the Seattle Longitudinal Study (Schaie & Willis, 2010), followed a group of people over the course of several decades. The cognitive abilities of some in the group declined rapidly with age, while those of others showed little change. Schaie discovered that the ones who showed little decline were those who challenged their brains throughout life. There was a correlation between people's ability to maintain their cognitive fitness and their level of education, high socioeconomic status, complex and intellectually challenging work, social engagement, and flexibility of personality.

> *Education is the best provision for old age.*
> Aristotle

One way to stimulate your brain is to perform familiar actions with your nondominant hand; this can form new neural pathways and strengthen the connectivity between neurons. If you're right-handed, try brushing your teeth, eating, or writing with your left hand on a regular basis.

> *Stimulating the brain makes it grow in every conceivable way.*
> Dr. Norman Doidge

Cognitively Stimulating Activities (a partial list)

- Critical thinking (interpreting proverbs)
- Analytical thinking (finding commonalities and differences)
- Exercises for verbal fluency; word-forming
- Learning and applying mnemonic strategies to remember names, tasks, information
- Solving math or reasoning problems
- Learning a second language (including sign language)
- Playing or learning to play a musical instrument
- Traveling
- Attempting to do things with your nondominant hand (brushing your teeth, buttoning your shirt, eating, texting, etc.)
- Solving jigsaw, Sudoku, and other puzzles
- Playing computer games designed to exercise attention, memory, speed of processing
- Learning to build or repair things
- Dancing, especially if it involves learning new steps and routines
- Playing tournament bridge, chess, or other games involving memory

It is essential to keep your brain healthy and trained to maintain its capacity and push back the effects of aging as much as possible. Studies using brain imaging, such as PET and fMRI, showed patterns of increased brain efficiency, especially in the frontal cortex, when those being studied engaged in training involving mental aerobics or memory enhancement strategies (Small & Vorgan, 2008).

Many people enjoy doing crossword puzzles, but there does not appear to be any evidence that this improves memory. However, it does improve the ability to find words (fluency).

Individuals with mild cognitive impairment (MCI) have a higher risk of progressing toward Alzheimer's disease, so it is especially important for them to engage in lifestyle practices for a healthy brain. Canadian researchers found that people with MCI who had engaged in brain-training interventions showed activation in several additional brain regions during memory tests and improved their scores on the tests (Deweerdt, 2011). Researchers agree it's never too late to begin building cognitive reserve. Continual learning builds brain circuitry.

> *Let us all do what is right, strive with all our might toward the unattainable, develop as fully as we can the gifts God has given us, and never stop learning.*
> Ludwig van Beethoven

Brain SENSE Log

Research shows that engaging in certain lifestyle behaviors can help you maintain brain health. Keep track of your practices in the chart below for at least one week, to see if you are engaging in all the healthy behaviors at least a few times per week. If you wish to log more than a week, make copies of the chart before completing it.

Week of _____

Category	Mon	Tues	Wed	Thurs	Fri	Sat	Sun	Total per week
Socialization hours								
Exercise/Physical Activity hours								
Nutrition: Servings of fruits/veggies								
Nutrition: Servings of Omega-3's								
Nutrition: Servings of glasses of water								
Nutrition: Servings of foods high in fat or sugar [1]								
Sleep hours								
Spirituality hours [2]								
Education hours [3]								

Notes:

1. Foods high in fat or sugar should be avoided.
2. Spirituality includes number of hours in prayer, meditation, worship, study, etc.
3. Education includes the number of hours stimulating the brain with novel and complex ideas and/or learning.

Chapter Four
Remembering and Forgetting: What's Age Got to Do with It?

Review of Chapter Three
1. What lifestyle practices do the letters in the acronym *SENSE* represent? (p. 23)
2. Why is exercise important for brain health? (p. 24)
3. What foods should you eat for better brain health, and what foods should you avoid? (p. 29)
4. Why is sleep important for brain health? (p. 34)
5. What are three cognitively stimulating activities you can incorporate into your lifestyle? (p. 41)

When you can't remember someone's name or where you put something, have you ever worried that your memory is starting to go? This chapter explains the typical changes in memory and thinking most of us will experience as we age. You will be cautioned about illusions of learning: use of ineffective strategies which lull you into thinking you have learned and therefore can later remember something, when in most likelihood you cannot. The various reasons we forget or misremember are also explained.

> *The existence of forgetting has never been proved: we only know that some things do not come to mind when we want them to.*
> Friedrich Nietzsche

Everything we have learned depends on our memory. Plato said, "All knowledge is but remembrance." The increasing prevalence of dementia, and specifically Alzheimer's disease, is devastating mostly because it results in loss of memory. Victims lose not only the ability to remember words, functions of objects, and their experiences; they eventually lose their ability to recognize their loved ones, and then ultimately lose their sense of self. Memory makes us who we are and gives meaning to "self." It also enables us to work, to play, to function on a day to day basis, and to learn. On the job, we not only need to acquire new information, procedures, and skills; we also need to make decisions and learn from our mistakes. Imagine for a moment what your daily life would be like without memory. For starters, you would not even be able to comprehend the words on this page.

> *Life is all memory, except for the one present moment*
> *that goes by so quick you hardly catch it going.*
> Tennessee Williams

Illusions of Learning

I love yellow highlighters! When I read nonfiction books, I highlight as I read. Then, when reviewing the content, I just reread the highlighted parts. This often leaves me thinking, "I know this!" Unfortunately, many readers have this same thought, but it is not necessarily accurate. Reading and rereading text results in greater fluency, meaning the reading becomes easier. In addition, the content becomes familiar, creating the illusion that one "knows" or has learned it. But recognizing something because it is familiar is no guarantee that you will later be able to recall it, which requires searching for and retrieving it from your long-term memory.

A better method to ensure you will learn something is to review what you have highlighted using strategies such as *elaborative rehearsal* or *generating questions*. The elaborative rehearsal method involves thinking about the meaning of what you read or making connections between the new information and your prior knowledge about similar content. Generating questions involves thinking up questions which can be answered by the material you read and using these to test yourself on the content. Regularly practicing elaborative rehearsal and question generation can help ensure that you have, in fact, learned what you read, leading to a higher probability of being able to recall it later.

> *We are who we are in good measure because of*
> *what we have learned and what we remember.*
> Nobel Laureate Dr. Eric R. Kandel

Age-Related Cognitive Changes

Cognitive changes that accompany normal aging are referred to as "age-associated memory impairment" (AAMI) or "age-related cognitive decline" (ARCD). Some changes begin as early as age 30, but most begin in the mid-40s or the 50s. Individuals vary widely in terms of how their cognitive function changes as they age. There is a larger difference between the lowest and highest functioning people in groups of older adults (e.g., 65- to 85-year-olds) than in groups of younger adults (20- to 40-year-olds).

Ways in Which Aging Affects Attention and Memory

- Speed of processing slows, so encoding and recalling information takes longer.
- Perception (especially visual and auditory) generally diminishes, resulting in less effective and/or incomplete encoding.
- Working memory (ability to hold and manipulate information in mind) is reduced.
- Sustaining attention (especially to detail) for long time periods is more difficult.
- Sensitivity to interference increases, ability to inhibit distractions decreases, and multi-tasking becomes more challenging.
- Source memory (recalling where one learned something) deteriorates.
- Difficulty retrieving names and vocabulary words (tip of the tongue!) occurs more frequently.
- Knowledge, vocabulary, reasoning, and wisdom remain strong and may improve!

Brain Break

An elderly gentleman in his 90s, very well dressed and groomed, walks into an upscale cocktail lounge. He sits at the bar beside an attractive woman in her 80s and says, "So tell me, do I come here often?"

Speed of Processing

Speed of processing refers to how fast we can think and process information and as we age, most of us will experience slower information processing. Storing information in memory and retrieving it may take longer than when we were younger. One reason for this is that myelin, the insulating fatty substance that coats axons, wears down with age. Myelin works similarly to insulation on electrical wires: it helps speed information transmission along the axon to the dendrites and on to other neurons. As myelin degrades, the signals travel more slowly.

A study of older air traffic controllers revealed that their reaction times, as well as their attention and memory skills, were worse than those of younger controllers. However, the older workers outperformed the younger on realistic, complex tasks. It appears that their years of experience contributed to their ability to juggle multiple bits of information and compensated for any cognitive decline in their brains (Nunes & Kramer, 2009). So, for these older adults, slower processing speed on this task did not put them at a disadvantage.

Perception

We experience our world primarily through our senses, so *perception* is very important, especially visual and auditory. As we age, we begin to experience changes in these senses. Visual changes related to age tend to start in our forties, when many of us begin to need reading glasses. Later, many people develop cataracts, with smaller percentages developing macular degeneration or glaucoma.

Hearing also diminishes in many older adults. Approximately 48 million Americans have some hearing loss, including about half of those over age 75 and about 25% of those between 60 and 69. The average age of first-time hearing aid wearers is 70, but many people wait 15 years from the time they know they have hearing loss until they purchase their first hearing aids. Of those age 70 and older who could benefit from wearing hearing aids, fewer than 30 percent have ever used them. As a result, these individuals may have difficulty communicating with others. Diminished hearing may lead to social isolation and depression, both of which can negatively impact brain health (Amieva et al., 2015). Fortunately, new hearing aid technologies are being developed, such as battery-free models, or models with technical refinements that adjust for feedback (like whistling or hissing noises), making them more appealing.

Forgetting

> *Memory is like a wax tablet. As we remember, we etch lines and patterns in the soft surface; then time, a great eraser, slowly smooths the lines away, causing us to forget.*
> Plato
> *The wisest man I ever knew taught me something I never forgot. And although I never forgot it, I never quite memorized it either. So what I'm left with is the memory of having learned something very wise that I can't quite remember.*
> George Carlin

Why do we forget? Most often, it is because we never actually *encoded* the information. If we were not paying attention when the information was presented, then it did not enter short-term or working memory, and so had no opportunity to be encoded into long-term memory. We can expect memory lapses when our emotions take over or when the situation does not allow us to sustain attention. This often happens when we are rushing, anxious, self-absorbed, or under stress.

Distractions and interruptions are notorious for causing us to forget, and we are more likely to experience forgetting when tired or drowsy, ill, or operating on "automatic" while in familiar surroundings. Sometimes these conditions can't be avoided, and if we are forgetful in them, instead of expressing frustration by saying, "I forgot," we might try saying:

- "I wasn't paying attention."
- "I didn't listen."
- "I did not make it a point to remember."

If something *has* been encoded, forgetting can result from decay or fading of the memory trace over time, especially for information we seldom use or access. Forgetting can be a good thing; what would life be like if you could remember all the experiences you've ever had? A waiter or waitress would remember all the orders of every customer ever served. What good would this information be?

> *Better by far that you should forget and smile*
> *than that you should remember and be sad.*
> Christina Georgiana Rossetti

A.R. Luria wrote a book called *The Mind of a Mnemonist*, about his subject, the Russian mnemonist Shereshevskii (referred to as "S"). A *mnemonist* is someone with the ability to remember unusually long lists of data—such as unfamiliar names, lists of numbers, or entries in books. After 30 years, he could recall word for word long passages he had learned earlier. S had a mind like a screen, full of images representing almost everything he encountered. He suffered greatly because he could *not forget* many insignificant details.

Consider the more contemporary example of the small group of adults with Highly Superior Autobiographical Memory (HSAM), the ability to recall the slightest details of nearly every day they have lived. There are at least 60 known cases worldwide, including the actress Marilu Henner (2013). If you give someone with HSAM a year, they will be able tell you what day of the week their birthday fell on in that year. People with HSAM are no better than normal when it comes to remembering things like faces or phone numbers, nor do they have photographic memory. Remembering too much information can clutter the mind and cause disorganization. It's important to *consciously decide* what information is *significant enough* to put into our memory system to be retrieved when needed.

> *Memory is the thing you forget with.*
> Alexander Chase

How Fast Do We Forget?

Research shows that we do not forget at a constant rate, but that *most* forgetting occurs soon after learning. The *rate* of forgetting then slows down and levels off as time passes.

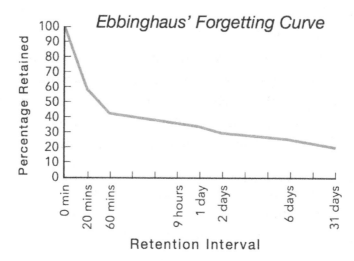

For example, people who studied Spanish in high school or college forgot:

- most of what they had learned (60%) within three years
- a little more (about 5%) over the next 50 years (Bahrick, 1984)

In another study (Bahrick et al., 1975), 400 participants were tested on memory of names and faces of people from their high school graduating classes, with a retention interval ranging from two weeks to 57 years.

- *Recall* of names went from about 15% to 6%.
- *Name recognition* was 90% at three months and didn't decline noticeably until 15 years later.
- *Face recognition* remained in the 80-90% range until about 35 years later.

This shows that material that is learned *very thoroughly* or is *very important* to us *may* be retained all our lives, especially if it was acquired over a long time (such as a four-year period during high school). Recognition is usually stronger than recall.

Overlearning refers to learning or memorizing something beyond the point of proficiency or immediate recall. This usually leads to persistence of the learning or memory over time. *Distributed practice* research shows that learning is more permanent if it is spaced over a longer period rather than done in a concentrated period (*massed practice*). For example, it is more effective to study something for 15 minutes a day over six days than for 90 minutes on one day. That is why cramming is not generally helpful for recalling information long term.

In a survey, memory experts and other cognitive neuroscientists unanimously *disagreed* with the statement that "human memory works like a video camera, accurately recording the events we see and hear so that we can review and inspect them later" (Simons & Chabris, 2011). The problem is that about two-thirds of the general population believes this is true. It is especially troublesome in courtrooms, because juries are generally formed using people from the general population.

> *The brain constructs and reconstructs information, creating a*
> *highly personal mental artifact and calling it memory.*
> Jeremy Campbell

However, human memory does not operate as if it were a video camera. A memory is constructed from stored and available bits of information; the brain unconsciously uses inferences to fill any gaps in the information. When all the fragments are integrated into a whole that makes sense, they form what we call a memory. In Daniel Schacter's book (2001), *The Seven Sins of Memory*, he explains the various ways in which our memories can be incomplete, biased, inaccurate, fabricated, inaccessible, and/or implanted.

Errors of Omission

The following errors occur when we fail to recall a desired fact, event or idea.

Encoding Failure

This occurs when information does not get stored in long-term memory.

Transience

This refers to the tendency to forget details about facts or events over time. We might say that a memory has "faded."

Absentmindedness

Most of us probably have done something absentmindedly at some time in our lives. The question is, why? Of course, the explanation is in the word itself: your mind was absent. Hence, you either forgot to do something you should have, or did something you shouldn't have. This often results from automaticity; behaviors or routines that have been performed numerous times become "automatic," and therefore do not require conscious attention. Pressing the button in your car to close the garage door as you leave your house is something you do routinely, and therefore without attention. When you are halfway down the street and wonder whether you did, in fact, press it, you most likely have no memory of having done it. You may drive back to your house only to discover that the garage door is closed! Or perhaps you intend to stop at the dry cleaners on your way home from work, but then realize you are home without your dry cleaning. Your brain had been automatically doing what it normally does after work: driving your route to home.

Absentmindedness involves failing to remember information that was never encoded properly or goes unnoticed when we need to retrieve it. Attention is generally required for something to be encoded in memory. To avoid being absentminded, we need to focus our attention. We may need to form a mental image of where we place something, for example our keys. We could even say out loud where we are placing them (e.g., "I am putting the keys on the table.") to have a better chance of later recalling where they are.

Blocking

Blocking is the most common form of memory lapse and occurs when we cannot access the word or name we are trying to recall, though we are sure it is in our memory. William James (1893) first drew attention to those peculiar experiences involved in trying to recall a forgotten name, knowing/feeling how close we are to retrieving it, being aware of names we do retrieve that are wrong, but not being able to retrieve the correct ones. Brown and McNeill (1966) called this phenomenon "tip-of-the-tongue" (TOT) behavior. Among the first to research this, they found that when people were presented with definitions of low-frequency words that are generally easily recognized but not so easily retrieved, participants correctly recalled the number of syllables in the words about 60% of the time, the initial letter of the target word about 57% of the time, and words which sounded like the target words 48% of the time. The most naturally occurring TOTs are triggered by names of personal acquaintances, famous persons, and objects, and it is estimated that about half of TOTs resolve within a minute of the blocking experience.

In his book Schacter notes that the concept of blocking exists in 51 languages and suggests that word-retrieval failures occur less as a result of the loss of relevant memories, and more because irrelevant ones come to mind. Often, we can recall everything we know *about* a person or word, except the name or word itself.

The TOT experience is nearly universal; it has been found to occur in people of all ages. The frequency of TOT experiences does tend to increase with age, which often raises concerns about memory decline (Huijbers et al., 2017). However, these researchers demonstrated that age-related TOT experiences and memory failure are partially independent processes, and most studies conclude that the increase in frequency of TOTs in older adults does not predict later cognitive decline.

When you have a TOT experience, don't stress; this will only block memory. Instead, try to think of associated information. When trying to retrieve a person's name, think about where you last socialized with him/her, or facts such as career or place of employment, town where he/she resides, spouse, children, etc. Retrieving these related facts may help your brain locate the name for which you are searching.

TOT (Tip-of-the-Tongue) Exercise (See Answer #2, page 137)

Read the definitions below, and write the appropriate word if you know it, or DK if you don't know it. If you are reasonably certain you know the word, but can't recall it, write TOT for "tip-of-the-tongue," along with information about the word that comes to mind, such as the letter it starts with, the number of syllables, or a similar sounding word.

1. A stone having a cavity lined with crystals.

   _____

2. A great circle of the earth passing through the geographic poles and any given point on the earth's surface.

   _____

3. An adjective describing a tree that loses its leaves each year (opposite is *evergreen*).

   _____

4. A special quality of leadership that captures the popular imagination and inspires unswerving allegiance.

   _____

5. The red coloring matter of the red blood corpuscles.

   _____

6. A picture form of writing used in ancient Egypt.

   _____

7. A small, hard-shelled ocean dwelling animal that attaches itself to rocks and ships.

   _____

8. A person appointed to act as a substitute for another.

   _____

States and Capitals Exercise (See Answer #3, page 137)

Without looking ahead, search your memory to find, then write, the capital of each of these states (*free recall*):

Arizona	_____	Ohio	_____
California	_____	Pennsylvania	_____
Nevada	_____	Rhode Island	_____
New York	_____	Texas	_____

Below are the first letters of the capitals of the states; see if having these *retrieval cues* triggers your memory for the names of the capitals you could not recall.

Arizona	P _____		Ohio	C _____	
California	S _____		Pennsylvania	H _____	
Nevada	C _____		Rhode Island	P _____	
New York	A _____		Texas	A _____	

Errors of Commission

The following errors occur when a form of memory is present but is incorrect.

Bias

Bias occurs when our current knowledge, beliefs, and feelings distort our memories of earlier experiences. Have you ever had a discussion with a sibling or spouse about an event from the past in which each of you has a different recollection about what happened? This is caused by *bias*, since each person's unique interpretation of the event causes it to be stored differently in memory, and/or because subsequent experiences and/or emotions may have caused your memories or those of your sibling or spouse to change.

Suggestibility

Suggestibility refers to the vulnerability of our memory to being distorted by the power of suggestion. Leading questions and/or things seen, heard, or read can color our memories or even "create" them. Being exposed to new information after witnessing an event can change our memory of the event. Elizabeth Loftus has conducted experiments using "misleading information" (Loftus, 1979). In one, she showed participants a film about a traffic accident and then asked questions about what they had seen. Some were asked, "About how fast were the cars going when they smashed into each other?" while others were asked, "About how fast were the cars going when they hit each other?" The former question, which only differed by one word (*smashed* vs. *hit*) elicited a much higher estimate of speed. One week later they were asked additional questions, the critical one being, "Did you see any broken glass?" In the group that heard the word *hit*, 14% reported seeing broken glass, while in the group that heard the word *smashed*, 32% said there was glass. There was *no* glass. When misleading information is incorporated into and changes one's memory of an event, it is referred to as the *misinformation effect*.

One example of either lying or inaccurate recall is when Brian Williams, a prominent television news anchor, told various versions of a story about his experiences during the U.S. invasion of Iraq in March of 2003. His serial misstatements could have been the product of unintentional memory distortion. As will be described later, even memories for highly emotional events like the *Challenger* explosion or the 9/11 attacks can change substantially. With the passage of time we may remember the *gist* of an experience, but not the details—or whether we experienced the events *or* just heard about them. Perhaps you recall having slammed your hand in a car door as a child, only to get into an argument over whether it happened instead to your sister. Neuroscientists are still working to understand all the brain mechanisms behind memory formation and distortion.

False Memory Activity (an aspect of Suggestibility)

Read the words in the box below, then cover the list:

sheets	mattress	comfortable	pillow	blanket	room	dream
lay	chair	tired	rest	night	dark	time

Was the word *pillow* on the list? What about the word *tired? Sleep?*

If you recalled that *sleep* was on the list, you are a victim of *false memory*. Since many of the list words are related to sleep in some way, the brain makes the *inference* that the word *sleep* was also on the list, which it was not, creating a *false memory*.

Eyewitness Testimony and False Memory

In 2014, Michael Brown, a young, unarmed man in Ferguson, MO, was fatally shot by a police officer in broad daylight. Eyewitnesses gave dramatically different accounts of the events. Memory is subject to failures to encode, distortions, biases, misattributions of the source, and forgetting. Memory for an event may contain both accurate and inaccurate information, making it difficult to know whether a person is lying or just recalling inaccurately.

How we perceive the world is driven not only by what enters our brain through our eyes and ears, but also by our expectations. These "top-down" influences drive what we attend to and what we see but are themselves influenced by our past experiences. Two people with different backgrounds can witness the same event and "see" it differently. Even if two people see an event from the same vantage point, there is no guarantee they will remember it the same way or that either of them will be accurate when recalling it later. Often, if you ask a person to recount an event twice, separated by some amount of time, key details will be altered. When residents of New York were asked about their memories of 9/11 a year after the event, 40% of the details differed from their original accounts.

After Jennifer Thompson-Cannino was raped in 1984, she identified a man in a police lineup as her attacker. The officer conducting the lineup told her she had done a "good job," confirming that she'd picked the suspect. In two trials in 1985 and 1987, Ronald Cotton was convicted of rape and burglary largely based on the victim's misidentification. In May of 1995, DNA testing proved that Cotton had been wrongfully convicted. The real attacker, later identified by DNA evidence, had gone on to rape six more women. Cotton, after serving more than a decade in prison, met his victim. She and Cotton later wrote a book together, *Picking Cotton*, and have travelled the country telling audiences how this can happen. DNA has now exonerated more than 362 people (www.innocenceproject.org). Eyewitness misidentification has played a role in more than 70% of wrongful convictions later overturned by DNA testing.

In many of the cases where eyewitnesses were wrong, the real perpetrator was not in the initial lineup. If a person in a lineup looks like the perpetrator, a witness can identify the perpetrator and be highly confident. Functional brain scans cannot tell true from false memories with any kind of confidence. False memories are "memory illusions" akin to visual illusions. The powerful effects of visual illusions demonstrate how our brain takes shortcuts in how we see, and false memories show that our brain takes similar shortcuts in how we remember. Researchers have repeatedly created entirely false memories in the laboratory, such as convincing people that they had once been lost in a shopping mall as children.

Misattribution

Misattribution is a type of memory distortion or inaccuracy involving the *source* of a memory, such as when we erroneously attribute a recollection to the wrong time, place, or person. This occurs when you *can* remember informational content but *cannot* recall where you heard or learned it. For example, you may think you learned some information from watching television, when you heard it from a friend. This may explain why, when you tell a friend a joke, the friend tells you that *she* is the person who told you that joke several weeks ago! This can also explain déjà vu, which is a misattribution of current experience to the past, and how imagining an event can lead to believing that one experienced it.

A woman in Australia accused psychologist and memory expert Dr. Donald Thompson of having raped her. Thompson had an airtight alibi as he was doing a live interview for a TV program the victim had been watching just prior to the assault. The woman had seen the program and apparently misattributed her memory of him from the TV screen to the rape.

Flashbulb Memory

Flashbulb memories are "memories for the circumstances in which one first learned of a very surprising and consequential (or emotionally arousing) event" (Brown and Kulik, 1977). The term is so named because it seems as if the mind has taken a photograph of the circumstances in which the news was learned. The most compelling flashbulb memories tend to involve shocking historical events, such as the assassinations of John F. Kennedy and Martin Luther King, the *Challenger* explosion, and the September 11th attacks.

Neisser (Lindzey & Runyan, 2007) claims we develop flashbulb memories almost as if a camera flash went off and permanently "fixed" in our minds the image of what we experienced or observed. Most people will report that they can recall exactly where they were and what they were doing at the time of the event (or of learning of it). I vividly recall being at the local reservoir on the morning of September 11, 2001, walking on the path with my neighbor, when a woman rollerblading past stopped and told us that two planes had crashed into the World Trade Center Towers in New York. I recall the sky being a clear, bright, cloudless blue, with the sun shining brightly. It had been, up until that time, a beautiful day. Then this awful news ruined it. That memory is etched permanently and accurately in my brain. Or so I believe.

Neisser reports research he conducted on "flashbulb memories" that may shock you – as it does me. This research centers on the disastrous explosion of the space shuttle *Challenger* on January 28, 1986. The next morning, Neisser gave a questionnaire about how they learned of the event to a large freshman class. Nearly three years later he asked those who were still at Emory to recall how they first had heard about the *Challenger* disaster. The results were quite surprising. A few students remembered the circumstances well, but a substantial number reported highly confident memories that were nevertheless completely different from what they had written the day after the event. One student recalled that a girl had run screaming through her dorm shouting, "the space shuttle blew up," whereas her original account was of hearing about the disaster from friends at lunch (Lindzey & Runyan, 2007).

Memory Block Activity

Try to remember an event from 10 years ago, and write down everything you recall about it, not as narrative—just words or phrases that label each aspect of the event. Then use other sources to further jog your memory (photos, talking to someone else who was there, etc.). See if the additional retrieval cues help you recall more details.

Memory Circle Activity

When you want to recall an elusive name, event, or fact, start by relaxing. Then:

1. Get a blank piece of paper and draw a circle in the center.
2. Try to recall all the associations to the missing piece of information that you can and write them in the circle. For example, if it is a name, try to remember the last time you saw this person (or perhaps the first, when you were introduced), where and when this occurred, the surroundings, other people there, topics of conversation, etc.
3. As you build a network of information related to the missing piece of information (all inside the circle), it may lead you to recalling the elusive name, event, or fact.

Reminiscence Activity

Ask yourself, and then answer, questions about your past regarding:

- The house in which you grew up
- Your grandparents, aunts and uncles, cousins
- Your best childhood friends
- Your favorite teacher
- Hobbies, clubs, or sports in which you participated
- Learning to drive
- Your first date
- Your first job
- Your most exciting vacation

You may find it helpful to look at photographs, if available, or read diaries or journals if you kept any.

Chapter Five
How Memory Works

Review of Chapter Four
1. What are some of the ways aging affects the brain and memory? (p.45)
2. Explain blocking or "tip-of-the-tongue" (TOT) experiences. (p. 50)
3. Why is eyewitness testimony often not reliable? (p. 53)

In this chapter, you will learn how memory works: how your brain takes in information from your environment and makes it a part of who you are. You will also learn about the indispensable role attention plays in forming memories, and how to encode information so it will be easier to retrieve when needed.

The Information Processing Model of How Memory Works

To explain *how* memory works, Atkinson and Shiffrin (1968) proposed what later became known as the "boxes" model of memory, illustrated below.

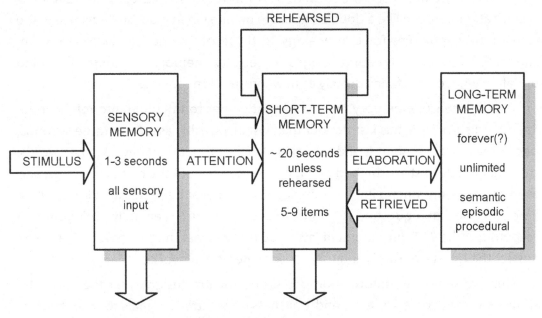

Sensory Memory (SM) briefly holds information coming to your brain through your senses. Information you pay attention to enters Short-Term Memory (STM), but only stays there for about 20 seconds unless you keep repeating it (rehearsal). STM can generally hold only about 5 to 9 items, or chunks, of information. Working Memory (WM) refers to the conscious (attending to, concentrating on) processing (manipulating, making calculations or decisions) of information. To store information in Long-Term Memory (LTM) so that you can later retrieve it, you need to intentionally use strategies such as organization, elaboration, and visualization. LTM storage is not limited, but information does not necessarily stay there forever. Sometimes it is there but cannot be accessed due to insufficient retrieval cues.

Sensory Memory (SM)

Information from our environment comes to our brain through the senses, so the first stage of memory processing is referred to as *Sensory Memory (SM)*. This ostensibly contains everything we see, hear, smell, taste and touch.

Research has demonstrated that at this stage of processing, memory is extremely brief. *Visual* sensory memory (what we take in through our eyes) is thought to last less than a second. This is good design, because it means that when I look in one direction and then quickly look in another, the image that I saw first has faded by the time I see the second. If this were not the case, I would see both images at once, much like a double exposure on film when it doesn't advance in the camera. (My apologies for that analogy to those of you not familiar with a film camera!) Information creating images in sensory memory is continually being updated; what enters fades quickly as new information replaces it.

Auditory sensory memory processes what comes to the brain through hearing. Psychologists believe this lasts longer than visual, possibly as long as three seconds, because we process sound, and especially language, *sequentially*. In other words, the brain needs to store the beginning of a sentence until the rest of it arrives, and then we can comprehend it. For example, have you ever been sitting at home when a person calls out a question to you from another room? Generally, isn't your first response, "What?" Then a moment later, you realize what the person asked, and can answer the question. This is auditory sensory memory at work.

Our *five senses* are information gatherers; each is designed for the particular stimulus it receives, translates, and transmits as electrical signals for our brain to process.

- *Sight* receptors work by interpreting light collected by the retina.

- *Smell and taste* work by chemical interpretation by the nerve cells of our olfactory system and the taste-receptor clusters (taste buds) on our tongues.
- *Sound* interpretation is based on vibrations against our eardrums.
- *Touch* (the somatosensory system) involves thermoreceptors for temperature, nocireceptors for pain, and mechanoreceptors for pressure and distortion.

The reason our senses have such a strong connection to memory is because the light, vibration, chemical, temperature, movement, and pain signals are "recorded" in our sensory receptors.

What we pay attention to from all these stimuli entering visual and auditory sensory memory determines what moves to Short-Term Memory for further processing.

Why Odors Trigger Memories and Emotions

Have you ever noticed how smelling something—a flower, perfume, or something cooking or baking—often results in your sudden recall of a prior experience? Odors are processed by the olfactory bulb inside the nose, which runs to the brain and is connected to the limbic system. The limbic system is comprised of the amygdala, which processes emotions, and the hippocampus, which stores memory. Information from our other senses, such as vision, hearing, and touch, does not pass through the amygdala and hippocampus. This explains why our sense of smell, or olfaction, is often more likely to elicit memories and emotions. Studies have shown that odors are more successful at eliciting the feeling of "being brought back in time" than are images.

In some cases, researchers have found that memories triggered by an odor resulted in greater activity in the limbic system than memories triggered by the words associated with the odor. So, being presented with the scent of a rose would result in more activation of the amygdala and hippocampus than would seeing or hearing the word "rose." Pleasant odors can evoke positive emotions and memories of pleasant experiences, while negative odor-evoked memories, such as in post-traumatic stress disorder (PTSD), are very difficult to extinguish. Some studies showed that the ability of odors to trigger memories continues to function well in older adults.

Types of Memory

Term	Definition	Example
Sensory Memory (SM)	Retains information about one to three seconds, long enough for it to be recognized	Closing your eyes quickly while looking at a brightly lit scene; the image lingers briefly
Short-term Memory (STM)	Remembering information for about 20-30 seconds	Remembering a phone number long enough to dial it
Working Memory (WM)	Focusing attention on, storing, and manipulating information for a relatively short period of time (such as a few seconds); not completely distinct from short-term memory	Retaining the partial results while solving an arithmetic problem without paper, or baking a cake without making the unfortunate mistake of adding the same ingredient twice
Long-term Memory (LTM)	Remembering information for a long time, usually weeks or years	Remembering names, phone numbers, multiplication tables, foreign languages
Explicit Memory	Conscious recollection	Remembering states and capitals, friends' names
Procedural (Implicit) Memory	Unconscious recollection, muscle memory, memory for sequences of actions	Knowing how to tie shoelaces, drive a car, play an instrument, etc., without thinking about the steps involved
Episodic Memory	Memory of your experiences (personal, autobiographical)	Remembering what you ate for lunch yesterday, or past activities or events in which you have participated
Semantic Memory	Memory of facts and/or information you have learned	Knowing that there are 12 months in a year or that a collie is a dog
Prospective Memory	Remembering to do things in the future	Remembering to go to an appointment, mail a letter, or take medication at the right time

Short-Term Memory (STM)

STM is sometimes called *immediate memory;* it only lasts about 20-30 seconds and involves retaining information long enough to process or manipulate it, record it tangibly, or use an intentional strategy to store it in Long-term Memory. For example, if someone tells you his/her phone number, you can retain it long enough to write it down or to find a way to encode it into LTM, perhaps by associating the numbers in some meaningful way. If you repeat the number mentally or out loud while looking for paper on which to write it, this is called *maintenance rehearsal.* Sometimes *repeating* it enough times will enable you to commit it to LTM. STM is sometimes likened to the temporary impression you make when typing a document into a computer. It remains long enough for you to print it out but disappears unless you elect to "save" it, in which case it is stored, much like LTM.

You may have been successful with the six-digit string, but not so with the ten-digit string, because of STM's limited capacity before it gets overloaded (about five to nine items such as digits or words). According to a classic study on memory span (Miller, 1956), the capacity of STM is, as he called it, "the magical number seven, plus or minus two." Other studies found that the number changed depending on what was being recalled. With practice, you might be able to increase your STM capacity; this might also be aided by *chunking*. For example, if the first three digits in a ten-digit string is your area code, those three digits would become one chunk. Since you already have these stored, your task of storing and recalling digits would be reduced to seven digits—a more manageable number, since it is within the capacity range.

Digit Span Activity

Without looking at them, have a partner read you the digit strings (one line at a time) in the first column, at a rate of about one per second. For each, say or write the digits *in the same order* in which they were read. The capacity of STM does shrink with age, so do not feel badly if you are unable to succeed with the longer digit strings. Then have your partner listen to and recall the digit strings in the second column.

For You	For Your Partner
6 2 8 0	3 0 4 2
3 9 4 1 5	4 5 1 9 3
0 5 2 7 1 3	6 5 9 1 7 0
4 6 3 0 8 2 7	8 3 1 6 2 4 5
3 5 8 6 0 2 4 9	2 4 7 5 0 1 6 3

Backward Digit Span Activity

For these sequences, *without looking at them*, listen to the string of digits (read by a partner), then try to say them *in the reverse order* from the way they were read (*backward*). There are three of each length for you and for your partner.

Four-Digit Groups

For You	For Your Partner
1653	1786
2714	4139
9680	5012

Five-Digit Groups

For You	For Your Partner
92783	68357
48602	19842
95127	53601

Six-Digit Groups

For You	For Your Partner
136205	859021
637918	978216
290413	850319

Gnilleps (spelling words backwards)

Without looking at the words in the first column below, have a partner read them to you, one at a time. Try to spell each word backwards. Then read the words in the second column to your partner and have him/her spell them backwards without looking at them.

For You	For Your Partner
BRAIN	HEALTH
MEMORY	NEURON
MINDFUL	MEDITATE
ATTENTION	INFORMATION

Story Recall

For each story below (A, B, or C), read it, then repeat it without looking at it. Your recall does not have to be verbatim (word for word) but should be close enough to convey the meaning. If you can, have someone else read the sentences to you and check your recall accuracy. Attempt to recall one sentence at a time or more.

Story A

We enjoy travelling and recently took a trip to Alaska.

We saw glaciers, fjords, and wildlife.

The weather cooperated, and we had no rain.

The food and entertainment on our cruise were excellent.

Story B

We like music and recently attended an orchestra concert.

A soprano and a tenor sang arias.

The acoustics in the concert hall were outstanding.

We could see and hear well from our seats.

Story C

We have fun when our grandchildren visit.

They are full of energy.

We like to play games and watch movies with them.

Our house is never quiet, and we are tired when they leave.

Visual Memory Practice

Study the objects in the photo for *one minute*, then **cover** the photo and try to recall all 10 objects.

Working Memory (WM)

Multiply 3 x 28 mentally (without writing anything). While doing this, try to observe your brain's processes. You may notice that you visualize the numbers, almost as if you were seeing them written on paper. You may also "hear" a voice in your head saying the numbers, the intermediate multiplication products, the sums, and the final solution. This mental multiplication exercise requires your brain to use Working Memory (WM). WM involves the ability to hold and manipulate information in your mind while ignoring irrelevant distractions and intruding thoughts. For example, when given a problem like 3 x 28, your working memory needs to retain the problem while recalling the necessary multiplication facts from long-term memory. Performing the computation requires retaining the numbers within each step until the computation is completed. WM is like a project manager: coordinating the information coming into your brain, prioritizing and processing it so you can ignore what is irrelevant and attend to what is important, and holding onto information while you work with it. WM is critical to *executive function*, the processing your brain does to plan and regulate behavior.

WM can also be likened to a rubber band; some are large, and some are small, but all can be stretched. We are all born with a certain WM capacity, but we can stretch it through training. WM starts to decline in our 40s, when we can remember and work with fewer pieces of information. People in their 40s can process an average of five pieces of information, just one fewer than when they were 30. Part of the reason for this decline may be the gradual loss of white matter in the brain. One way to hold off WM loss is to remain socially engaged, along with practicing WM-building exercises (Alloway, 2013). Some of these exercises require you to retain words, numbers, or letters and then repeat them, sometimes in reverse order; others require you to mentally process information.

Sudoku Basics

Research has shown that declines in working memory performance are associated with aging. Sudoku has task demands that are similar to working memory processes, and a research study suggests that this game may have the potential to improve working memory performance in older adults (Grabbe, 2011).

Sudoku is a grid consisting of columns, rows and blocks. A typical Sudoku is a grid of 9×9 (i.e., 9 small boxes in each row, each column, and each block). For anyone just learning to solve this type of puzzle, it is better to begin with a grid of 4x4 and then 6x6.

The objective of Sudoku is to fill the missing digits into the grid. For 4×4 grids you use the digits from 1 to 4. For 6×6 grids, you use digits 1 to 6, and for 9×9-grids, digits 1 to 9. Each digit is used only once for every row, column, and block. (A block for the 4x4 is a 2x2 grid; for the 6x6 it is a 2x3 grid. There are four blocks in each 4x4 puzzle and six blocks in each 6x6 puzzle.)

Sudoku Solving Tips and Exercises (See Answer #4, page 137)

- *Start* by trying to complete the rows, columns, or blocks missing the fewest digits.
- Use *process of elimination* to determine which digits might be used to fill in the empty boxes.
- In some cases, you will reduce the possible choices to two digits, and then with trial and error you can deduce which of the digits goes in which box.

Try these to begin:

	3	4	
4			2
1			3
	2	1	

			3
3	2	4	
	4	3	2
2			

3	4	1	
		2	
			2
	1	4	3

When you have mastered the 4x4 Sudoku, try the more challenging 6x6 puzzles below:

5	6		2		3
1		3		4	
	3		1		2
6		2		5	
	4		5		1
3		1		2	

1		3		4	
	6		2		3
	4	6	3		1
3		2	4	6	
2		1		5	
	5		1		2

Anagrams Exercise (See Answer #5, page 138)

Anagrams are scrambled words. Solving anagrams mentally requires you to use Working Memory to visualize different orders of the letters.

Rearrange each group of letters below to form words, then write each word on the blank line in the paragraph below where it makes the most sense.

DLORE   LAMENT   MUTILATES   RENAL   XPMLOEC   LSNGIVO   VEERRES

_____

It is important to use your brain and _____ it with new and _____ ideas. Even the brains of _____ adults can _____ and grow, especially when doing _____ exercise like _____ anagrams. These are just some of the things you can do to build cognitive _____.

Rearrange and Categorize Exercises (See Answer #6, page 138)

Which two sets of letters below can be arranged into six-letter English words?

OMLAGA   _____

ATRUNE   _____

FASUPA   _____

NINEGE   _____

Solve these anagrams to form words (Hint: They relate to this book's topics.)

RNBIA   _____

GANIG   _____

ESSTIERAGT   _____

BPEOMLR   _____

Which of the following scrambled words is the "odd man out" when the words are unscrambled, and why?

CGHICOA   _____

TTOOORN   _____

IMMIA   _____

CPOEHNANGE   _____

Rearrange the following letters to make a word and choose the category—*city*, *ocean*, *vegetable* or *flower*— in which it fits.

AIGNAHSH   _____

Musical Instrument Anagrams Exercise (See Answer #7, page 138)

Unscramble the letters in each box to form a word that is the name of a musical instrument.

1. JOABN   _____
2. LEULKEU   _____
3. NOVILI   _____
4. TELUF   _____
5. NOYLEXOPH   _____
6. NALTECIR   _____
7. UTIGRA   _____
8. ETOBRONM   _____

More Ways to Increase Working Memory Capacity

Play Chess

To play chess well, you must learn to expand WM capacity to hold a plan for several offensive moves while at the same time holding a memory of how the opponent could respond to each of the moves.

Use Rhythm

When you listen to a song, pay attention to and try to remember the beat, and see if you can play the rhythm later with spoons on your legs, or pencils or index fingers on a table or desk.

Count Coins

Put out an array of coins (start with two denominations, and then gradually increase it to four). Count all of each denomination in terms of how many there are of each, for example, 2 quarters, 4 dimes, 3 nickels, 7 pennies. Keep the tallies in your head. Or, add up the value of each denomination and calculate the total value of the coins. For example, 50 cents (2 quarters), 40 cents (4 dimes), 15 cents (3 nickels), 7 cents (7 pennies), results in a total of $1.12.

Do not write anything down and check your total against the coins.

Learn a Foreign Language

Research shows that bilinguals of all ages do better compared to monolinguals in a range of cognitive tasks, including WM. Consider taking a language class at a community college, checking out CDs from the library, or using an online program.

Long-Term Memory (LTM)

Long-term Memory is usually the goal for information we know we will need later, such as names of friends or coworkers, subjects studied in school, or numbers we use often and need to have handy. Sometimes information becomes stored in LTM because of repetition, the way most people memorize the multiplication tables. Emotions also impact what you pay attention to; your brain's limbic system governs emotions and decides what is important and what is not. If an emotion is attached to an event, the neurotransmitter norepinephrine is released, causing the memory to be encoded more strongly. Therefore, you are more likely to remember it and recall it more vividly for a longer period (Tully & Bolshakov, 2010).

Though STM has a limited capacity, LTM does not. In fact, the more you learn, the more you *can* learn. Your brain grows dendrites and expands neural networks as it acquires new information. An exception is that most people do not have clear memories of events from their early childhood (birth through three years); this is referred to as *infantile amnesia*. The capacity to form and verbally recall declarative memories gradually emerges as an infant develops (from about 24–36 months of age). For example, three-year-old children accurately recount "important" life events (such as a trip to McDonald's) when prompted. Although young children can acquire memories, they forget faster than older children. Infantile amnesia is thought to occur in part because memory retention increases gradually with age. Some explanations of infantile amnesia focus on memory retrieval and suggest that memories formed in childhood are permanently stored but simply cannot be accessed during adulthood. It has also been suggested that infantile amnesia reflects a developmentally critical period during which the learning system itself is learning how to learn and remember. In addition, it is possible that the lack of words and language at those young ages makes storage and retrieval of memories more difficult.

Once something is in your LTM, does it remain there for the rest of your life? An experiment to answer this question cannot be designed, but there is anecdotal evidence to support the theory that much of the information encoded in the past still resides in your memory. For example, Bahrick (1984) has shown that those who studied a foreign language, such as Spanish, for many years tend to be able to recall many vocabulary words years later, even if they have not been using the language regularly. Large portions of the originally-acquired information remained accessible for over 50 years, despite the fact the information was not used or rehearsed during that time span. In another study he found that, years after high school graduation, people were able to correctly recognize names associated with photos of high school classmates (Bahrick, 1975). This very slow forgetting process is attributed to the fact that names of classmates are learned and used over a period of four-or-so years, and hence are overlearned.

In *Remembrance of Things Past*, Marcel Proust recalls a time he was drinking tea and dipping a cookie into it. As soon as the wet cookie touched his palate, he felt something extraordinary happening: the present with its problems and weariness vanished, and a deep joy overwhelmed him. He waited eagerly, trying to understand what had caused it. A vivid memory suddenly came to mind: the long-ago taste of the cookie his aunt Leonie gave him when he, as a boy, would come to say "good morning" in her bedroom. This one memory, elicited by the taste of the cookie, triggered the recall of a chain of images of his happy childhood.

Sensory stimuli can serve as *retrieval cues* to recall sensations that were recorded in our past. It is speculated this is because the olfactory system for taste and smell is adjacent to the limbic system governing emotion. Try to recall times when an odor or taste (food cooking, flowers, cologne), or perhaps some music, served as a *retrieval cue* and awakened a long-buried memory for you. This retrieval cue most likely evoked a memory that you may not have consciously been able to retrieve, but effectively unlocked the "place" in your LTM where that memory was stored. We are sometimes unable to recall something, not because it has been forgotten, but because we lack the necessary *retrieval cue* to *access* it in our brain.

Semantic, Episodic, and Procedural Memory

Try to recall:
- your first day of school
- the first paying job you had
- the last time you ate ice cream
- the capital of France

How is the last recollection different from the first three?

The first three involve your personal, autobiographical experiences, while the last one may not, if you have never been to Paris. However, it may be autobiographical if you have memories of when you first learned it was the capital of France.

Declarative memory includes information about which we can say, "I know that...," such as "I know that today is Wednesday" or "I know that I ate a salad for lunch." It includes both *semantic* and *episodic memory*. *Semantic* refers to your encyclopedic knowledge of the world: facts, information, vocabulary, things you learn in school. We tend not to forget these as we age; in fact, most research has shown that our vocabulary tends to continue increasing with age.

Episodic refers to personal, autobiographical experiences, such as your first day of kindergarten, how you celebrated your last birthday, and what you ate for dinner last night. This can include everything from what you ate for breakfast today, to the movie you saw last week, to the gifts you received on your fifth birthday. Think of these as "episodes" in your life. We tend to be able to recall more of the autobiographical experiences that have an emotional component, whether positive or negative. If your first day of school was a bit traumatic, and you cried when your parent dropped you off and left, you may have a more vivid memory of it than if the experience went smoothly for you.

For routine experiences, it might be difficult to retrieve a specific instance; they may all run together. For example, if you generally eat turkey on Thanksgiving, you may believe you "recall" eating it two Thanksgivings ago, when in fact you may have had something else that year. Ulric Neisser (1981) calls this *repisodic memory*, meaning that we form a schema for events that we engage in routinely, and then recall more of an "ideal" representation rather than the exact experiences.

Semantic and *episodic* memory are considered *explicit*, because you must make a conscious effort to retrieve these memories. *Procedural* memory, also referred to as "motor" or "muscle" memory, is considered *implicit*, because these memories can be retrieved without conscious attention. A woman found wandering the streets, who was discovered to have amnesia, could not recall her name or phone number. However, when given a phone and asked to dial home, she did. This is an illustration of implicit, procedural memory; her fingers knew the order of keys to press even though she could not recall or state the phone number.

Procedural memory involves behaviors we engage in regularly, many of which become automatic because of repetition. These include tying a shoelace, driving a car, playing scales on a musical instrument, typing, and riding a bike. These memories are controlled largely by the regions of the brain that control motor function, such as the cerebellum. Think about learning a new dance: at first, you need to think almost continuously about where your feet are and when and where to move them. Once you have mastered the dance, your brain tends to carry out all the steps automatically, without your having to think about them.

Which of the memories below is episodic? Semantic? Procedural?
- Recalling the definition of the word *abstruse*.
- A memory of your last haircut.
- Remembering how to access voicemail on your phone.

Name List Recall Exercise (See Answer #8, page 138)

Practice recalling sequenced lists in different ways.

One example is the list of ten U.S. Presidents from Trump to Johnson:

Trump (R)

Obama (D)

Bush (R)

Clinton (D)

Bush (R)

Reagan (R)

Carter (D)

Ford (R)

Nixon (R)

Johnson (D)

Study the names and then, without looking at the list, recall them as follows:

1. In chronological order (least to most recent).
2. First only the Democrats, then only the Republicans.
3. In alphabetical order.

Paired Associates Activity

Learn the following word pairs by *repeating* the pairs several times. For example, if the pair is CAT-WINDOW, say over and over to yourself, "CAT-WINDOW, CAT-WINDOW." Set a timer for *one minute* (about 7 seconds per pair) and use repetition of the pairs to encode them into memory.

JAIL – CLOWN	LIZARD – PAPER
ENVELOPE – SHOE	KNIFE – BEAR
CANDY – MOUNTAIN	BOOK – PAINT
HAMMER – STAR	FLOWER – OCEAN

Without looking at the word pairs you studied, on the blanks below, write the associated word for each word shown.

ENVELOPE _____

FLOWER _____

CANDY _____

KNIFE _____

JAIL _____

BOOK _____

LIZARD _____

HAMMER _____

Visualization Exercise (See Answer #9, page 139)

1. In what hand does the Statue of Liberty hold the torch?

    _____

2. Is the angle formed by the hands of a clock at 3:05 larger than the angle formed at 8:20?

    _____

3. What shape are Mickey Mouse's ears?

    _____

4. Which is darker green, iceberg lettuce or spinach?

    _____

Mental imagery is like perception; we see objects and register shape, size, color. With mental imagery, stimulation is not coming directly from our sensory organs (eyes, ears, etc.) but arises from accessing information we have previously stored in memory. Questions 1 and 2 above activate the top-brain system (*spatial relations*) while questions 3 and 4 activate the bottom-brain system (*shapes and colors*).

Paired Associates Activity Using Imagery

For the following pairs, *visualize an image* in which the two objects are interacting. For example, if the pair is CAT–WINDOW, visualize a cat jumping through a closed window, shattering the glass. Just create an image and do not use any other study method. Take *one minute* to learn this list (about 7 seconds per pair).

SOAP – MERMAID	MIRROR – RABBIT
FOOTBALL – LAKE	HOUSE – DIAMOND
PENCIL – LETTUCE	CAR – HONEY
BREAD – GLASS	DOLLAR – ELEPHANT

Without looking at the word pairs you studied, on the blanks below, write the associated word for each word shown.

DOLLAR _____
BREAD _____
MIRROR _____
FOOTBALL _____
SOAP _____
CAR _____
PENCIL _____
HOUSE _____

Did you recall a greater number of words in this exercise, when you created mental images, than you did when you just used repetition to memorize the pairs?

Chapter Six
Attention and Mindfulness

Review of Chapter Five

1. About how long does short-term memory (STM) last, and about how many items (or chunks) of information can it usually hold? (p. 61)
2. How would you explain working memory (WM) to someone? (p. 64)
3. Long-term memories can be *semantic, episodic or procedural*. Give an example of each. (p. 69)

In this chapter you will learn about the cognitive skill of attention, and why it is so important to everything you do. You will also learn about the benefits of mindfulness and suggestions for practicing mindfulness regularly.

Attention

1. Look around you, making note of at least three to four items that are *green*. Now, close your eyes, and try to recall everything around you that is *blue*. This may be difficult; explanation to follow.
2. If you wear an analog watch, without looking at it, do you know if the six is an Arabic numeral, a Roman numeral, or just a line? Guess which it is, and then check to verify if your answer is correct.
3. Without looking at a penny, try to see if you can recall the following information about the *face* side of a penny (most people, other than coin collectors, will not be able to do this):
   - Is Lincoln facing right or left?
   - Is anything above his head? If so, what?
   - Is anything below his head? If so, what?
   - To the left?
   - To the right?

That was a *recall* task, which can be difficult. The next task involves *recognition*, which is generally somewhat easier.

In the array below, are you able to *recognize* the correct penny?

Each of these tasks serves to illustrate an important principle about memory. For information to get into your *short-term memory*, you need to pay attention to it! In the first task, you probably were more easily able to recall the green items you had paid attention to than blue items—which you may not even have noticed, especially since you were focusing on green.

In the second task, it is possible that you determine the time displayed on your watch by noting the hand positions. Oftentimes we only need to pay attention to the *position of the hands*, so we may not attend to and recall the *format* of the numbers around the watch face perimeter.

For the third task, though most of us have handled a penny countless times in our lives, we rarely need to look at the details on the coin. Unless we are collectors, we generally only *pay attention* to a penny's color and size; hence, the details and where they are located tend not to be in our memory. (The correct penny is A.)

The first strategy I would like to suggest for improving memory is to Pay Attention! This is the *P* of my acronym *PAVE* (which you will learn about in Chapter 8), which represents four strategies you should use regularly to improve memory. Attention is what helps us grab what is relevant from information entering *sensory memory* and get it into *short-term* or *working memory* for further processing.

> *The true art of memory is the art of attention.*
> Samuel Johnson

Have you ever listened to a class lecture or church sermon and noticed that you missed something because your mind wandered? Or after reading a page of a text, realized you have no idea of what you just read because you were thinking of something else? Since reading, once mastered, becomes an automatic activity, it is possible for our brain to read the words without registering the meaning, which may cause us problems!

Read the following riddle:

> As I was going to St. Ives,
> I met a man with seven wives,
> Each wife had seven sacks,
> Each sack had seven cats,
> Each cat had seven kits.
> Kits, cats, sacks, wives.
> How many were going to St. Ives?

What was your answer? Most of us focus on the numerous sacks, people, and animals mentioned and assume we must calculate a large number, but the "I" in the first line suggests that one person (the narrator) was *going to* St. Ives. Since the man and his wives, sacks, etc., were *met* by the narrator on the way *to* St. Ives, the trick of the riddle is that they were in fact *leaving*–not going to–St. Ives.

> *As a rule, we don't know when we are being inattentive.*

Attention is one of the most important cognitive processes and involves focusing on specific features of the environment or on certain thoughts or activities. Examples include searching for a specific house number while driving down a street or working on an important task while people are talking nearby. Attention can be likened to a *spotlight* which casts light on a limited area. This determines what we focus on and notice in our environment and is often influenced by *emotion*. If we are anxious or enthusiastic about something happening in our lives, we might be thinking about that instead of the task at hand. As a rule, we *don't know* when we are being inattentive!

Magicians earn their living by misdirecting attention, and the founders of a new discipline called *neuromagic* have been able to study how some of the world's greatest magicians trick the brain. Magic tricks work because the human process of attention is both "hardwired and hackable," according to researchers Macknik and Martinez-Conde (2010). Good magicians know that we have a limited capacity for attention, and they exploit this, not only by getting you to look somewhere they choose, but by using movement, patter, comedy and laughter.

Our ability to focus attention and to inhibit distractions declines with age, contributing to age-related memory loss. Research shows that attention training can change brain activity, giving healthy older adults a greater ability to block distractions and improve concentration.

Types of Attention

Selective Attention – Focusing one's attention on one stimulus or task.

Divided Attention – Attempting to pay attention to, or carry out, two or more different tasks simultaneously. To an extent, divided attention can be achieved with practice.

Controlled Processing – Processing that involves paying close attention.

Automatic Processing – Processing that occurs automatically, without the person intending to do it, and that uses few cognitive resources. Automatic processing is associated with easy or well-learned tasks. Recall learning how to drive a car. At first, you had to think about each step: put foot on brake, turn on engine, put car in drive, etc. Once mastered, you could just get into a car and go, without thinking of all these steps, and usually while thinking about something else! You went from using *controlled processing* while learning, to *automatic processing* once you mastered this skill. Most people can relate to being on "automatic pilot" while driving and ending up at home without having made the intended stop to pick up something at the grocery store.

> *If you can't pay attention, you can't learn.*
> *What you don't learn, you can't remember.*

Multitasking

If you are a sports fan, do you ever watch one game while listening to another? Are you truly catching everything about both games? Probably not. For the most part, *multitasking* is a myth: your brain is not doing the two tasks concurrently but is alternating attention and processing between the tasks. Multitasking *is* possible if your brain is using different areas for each task, such as watching TV while riding an exercise bike. Research on multitasking shows that, for all but about 2.5% of the population, the more people try to do at one time, the worse they perform. The brain is a sequential processor, and research shows that attempts to multitask usually result in a person needing more time to complete the tasks and making more errors than if each had been done alone (Rock, 2009).

Multitasking Activity

Count out loud from 1 to 10 as rapidly as you can, then recite the letters A–J, also out loud and rapidly. Notice how quickly and easily you can do each of these tasks.

Now, try to do *both* simultaneously (i.e., *multitask*), by alternating between the letters and the numbers (A, 1, B, 2, etc.). What did you notice? Did this take longer than the combined times for reciting first the numbers, then the letters? Did you make any mistakes?

Research shows that doing two tasks simultaneously often takes the brain *longer* and results in *more errors* than doing first one task and then the other. This happens because in multitasking, the brain is actually *switching attention* rapidly *between* the tasks. This takes time, and can result in errors.

Attention and Age

Dr. Paul Laurienti observes that as we get older, the challenges associated with inattentiveness grow. Deteriorating visual attention can affect behavior, such our ability to read or drive. Aging is usually accompanied by changes in how information gathered from the environment by our eyes and ears is perceived. Older adults combine information from the different senses more readily than do younger adults. This is called *sensory integration* and can lead to difficulties in blocking out distracting sights and sounds while still maintaining focus on important information (Wake Forest University Baptist Medical Center, 2007).

Dr. Laurienti led a research study which found that attention *training* can change brain activity, giving older adults a greater ability to block distractions and improve concentration. In one-on-one sessions, participants were asked to ignore distracting information as the tasks became more difficult during the eight-week training. The study authors concluded that attention training may be a way to improve sensory processing by reducing older adults' susceptibility to distracting stimuli.

What Factors Influence Attention?

Before reading further, identify what characteristics of things in your environment influence what you pay attention to.

_____

_____

_____

Some factors that influence our attention are:
Motion: Adults and children are more likely to pay attention to an object when there is motion involved. *Example:* Children are more attracted to toys that move.
Size: Objects or text that are larger attract more attention than normal or small objects. *Example:* Traffic signs are large and often use capital letters.

Intensity: Intense objects or text garner attention. *Example:* Bright colors attract more attention than plain black text.

Novelty: Stimuli that are novel or unusual in some way tend to draw our attention. *Example:* A person will pay more attention to a two-headed goat than a one-headed goat, because a two-headed goat is not something one sees every day.

Emotion: Words with strong emotional connections seem to elicit more attention than others. *Example:* In nursing school, if the teacher said, "This could *kill* your patient," probably all students would perk up and pay attention.

Personal Significance: We are more likely to pay attention to a person or concept that holds personal significance to us. *Example:* If a person has had a family member diagnosed with diabetes, he or she is more likely to pay attention to a lecture about diabetes in an attempt to learn something helpful to that relative.

Social cues: People are more likely to pay attention to things they see others looking at/reacting to. *Example:* If you see a crowd of people staring at something, you will try to find out what they find so interesting; it's human curiosity.

Working in Spite of Distractions

Your brain needs to be able to inhibit or stop itself from shifting focus from the project at hand to whatever in the environment (or in your mind) is presenting as distraction. This could be a phone ringing, the computer's sound that an email message has arrived, a conversation in the next cubicle, or even your own thoughts wandering to an unrelated topic. You need to learn to suppress a response of attention-shifting to remain focused on your work or task.

The Role of Emotion in Directing Attention

The *amygdala* is involved in evaluating information relevant to us and in directing our response. Unfortunately, the emotional areas of the brain can interfere with even simple cognitive responses. One study found that feeling anxious while doing math problems affected a task as simple as counting past five (Blair et al., 2007). The implication is that these emotional centers can interfere with attention and focus, thereby interfering with learning and memory. When we are reacting emotionally, it affects our thinking. Often more activity in the amygdala results in less activity in the neocortex (thinking brain) and the prefrontal cortex, whose job is to make rational decisions. However, studies have shown that we can be trained in the use of cognitive strategies to reduce negative emotions. One such study showed that the prefrontal cortex can dampen the activated amygdala, telling it, in essence, to calm down (Wager et al., 2008).

Basic Guidelines for Improving Focus and Attention

1. When someone is talking to you, *look at the person and listen closely*. If you miss something that is said, ask the person to repeat it or to speak more slowly.

2. *Paraphrase* what you heard to make sure that you understood it and to reinforce the information.

3. If you tend to get distracted during conversations, try socializing with people in *quiet environments*, such as homes instead of noisy restaurants. At a restaurant, sit near a wall, and ask your companions to sit against the wall so when you sit facing them, you won't have your attention distracted by other diners.

4. *Don't multitask!* You can improve your ability to focus on a task and screen out distractions if you do one thing at a time. If someone asks you something while you're in the middle of reading or working, ask if it can wait until you're finished. Try not to read incoming emails or answer phone calls until you've finished your task.

Word Riddles Exercise (See Answer #10, page 139)

Read each question carefully to figure out the answer, paying attention to possible alternative meanings.

1. What starts with "e" and ends with "e" and contains one letter?
2. What "room" has no door, no windows, no floor, and no roof? (Several answers are possible.)
3. What is found in the middle of Texas?
4. What is the difference between here and there?
5. This person is always wiring for money. Who is he?

Item Attributes Exercise (See Answer #11, page 139)

What do these three items have in common?

Attention to Detail Exercise (See Answer #12, page 139)

Bart and Bob, twin brothers, went to a bar. They both ordered scotch on the rocks and were served identical drinks. Bart nursed his drink while Bob gulped his down quickly. Within a few minutes of finishing their drinks, they both got sick. Bob recovered, but Bart died. Why?

Paying Attention and Following Instructions – Spatial Processing Activity

This activity, which exercises the brain's processes of visualization and comprehension of spatial information, requires a partner. You should use Diagram A and your partner, Diagram B. *Do not look at each other's diagrams.*

Describe Diagram A to your partner who, *without looking at it*, needs to draw it on a blank sheet of paper. You should give specific instructions to your partner, such as, "Near the top, and about an inch from the left edge of your paper, draw a circle that is about one inch in diameter." Your partner must listen and *pay close attention* to your instructions. When done, compare your partner's drawing with the diagram.

Then *reverse roles* so that your partner can describe Diagram B to you, and you can attempt to draw it without seeing it.

Diagram A

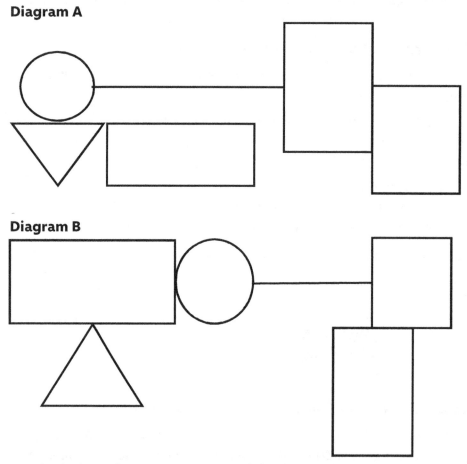

Diagram B

Think about the exercise you just did. What made it difficult? How could it have been made less difficult? What did you need to pay attention to when listening to the instructions?

Paying Attention and Following Instructions – Verbal Processing Exercise (See Answer #13, page 139)

The beginning of a saying is provided, along with instructions to follow to discover the ending. In the box provided, write all the letters for each numbered step according to the instructions. If done correctly, step 7 will have the ending.

1. The beginning of the phrase is NEVER TOO OLD.
2. Move the first letter to the end.
3. Remove the second E and two O's.
4. Move the T and O to the first and second positions.
5. Move the L to the third position.
6. Change the V to an A.
7. Remove the D.   *What is the ending of the saying?*

1. N E V E R T O O O L D
2.
3.
4.
5.
6.
7.

Spot the Differences Visual Attention Activity

This involves spotting differences between two similar photographs or drawings. Brain areas and cognitive processes involved:

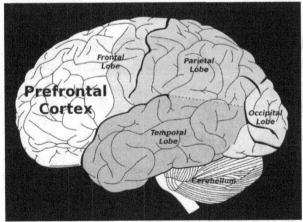

- *Occipital lobes* to identify the objects that you see
- *Occipital and parietal lobes* to analyze the spatial relationships between the objects

- *Short-term memory*, involving your *frontal and parietal lobes,* to remember what you see in one picture and compare it to what you see in the other
- *Frontal lobes* to mark the locations where you see a difference

There are apps and internet versions of this game, in which you are shown two images that seem identical, but several small details have been changed in one; your goal is to find all the differences between the images. Try to do this faster each time you play. (Search for "Game of Five Differences")

Can you find 12 differences between each of these pairs of pictures?
(See Answer #14, page 140)

(Reprinted with permission from www.comparrotpuzzles.com.)

Giraffe

Burro

Handyman

Continuity Errors and Change Blindness

Do you recall watching a movie or television show in which you noticed that a prop in one scene was missing from the next shot of the same scene, or where a person's clothing was different in some way? If items within a scene change place or disappear, that is referred to as a *continuity error*. This refers to the consistency of the characteristics of people, plot, objects, and places seen by a viewer over the course of the movie or show. In the classic film *Casablanca* (1942), there is a scene in which Humphrey Bogart is reading a note from Bergman, but it is dissolved by the heavy rain and he is dripping wet. In the next scene, he is standing on the step of a train, totally dry! In *Spider-Man* (2002), when Peter shoots his web at his bedroom lamp and pulls it across the room, it smashes against the wall and breaks. But when Aunt May is talking to Peter (who *is* Spider-Man) from the door seconds later, the lamp is back on the dresser, unbroken. There are numerous examples of continuity errors in movies, many of which we do not notice.

Not seeing continuity errors is an example of what psychologists call *change blindness*, or the inability to notice changes occurring right before our eyes. It can be very difficult to detect changes that take place in our environment. We tend not to store many details of a scene in memory, so to see an object change, it is necessary to attend to the object. *Change blindness* occurs because the system that processes visual information assumes that the world is stable and predictable. Change blindness can be a good thing for Hollywood, because many actors have doubles that stand in for them during dangerous stunts or for up-close nude shots. Unless they are intentionally looking for it, most movie viewers do not detect a double who is replacing an actor.

Distraction while Driving

Distracted driving refers to any behavior that results in a person's attention being diverted from the task of driving. *All* distractions endanger driver, passenger, and bystander safety. These types of distractions include:

- Texting
- Using a cell phone or smartphone
- Eating and drinking
- Talking to passengers
- Grooming
- Reading, including maps
- Using a navigation system
- Tuning a radio station

The National Conference of State Legislatures reports that more than 220 million people in the United States subscribe to wireless services, and an estimated 80 percent of those subscribers use their phones while driving. The National Safety Council reports that every day, at least nine Americans die and 100 are injured in distracted driving crashes. In 2016, the National Highway Traffic Safety Administration (NHTSA) reported that 3,450 people died in distraction-affected crashes, and 391,000 additional people were injured. Drivers who use hand-held devices are four times more likely to get into crashes serious enough to injure themselves, but hands-free cell phone use is not substantially safer than hand-held use. Text messaging creates a crash risk 23 times worse than driving while not distracted.

Everyone knows it is not smart to text and drive, and maybe not even to talk and drive, and yet many people still do it. What many do not know is how our brain can dupe us into thinking we can do several things at once with no consequences. We are so used to checking our phone numerous times per day that when it rings while we're driving, we may feel compelled to check it then, also. David Greenfield, an assistant clinical professor of psychiatry for the University of Connecticut School of Medicine, is the founder of the Center for Internet and Technology Addiction. His research tells us that when we hear a notification sound on our phone informing us we have an email or text, our brain gets a hit of *dopamine*, a chemical that increases arousal and energizes the reward circuits in our brain. The dopamine reward centers in the brain also govern pleasure from eating, from sex, and from drugs and alcohol.

Sometimes it is the *expectation* of a reward—that someone has texted you or has tagged you on Facebook—that leads to a higher shot of dopamine than the reward itself. Another problem is that when the brain reward center is activated by that dopamine elevation, it shuts down access to the prefrontal cortex, the part of our brain most responsible for reasoning and decision-making. In addition, each time nothing bad happens when we look at social media or text or do anything else while behind the wheel, it reinforces our belief that we will be safe if we do it again.

Cognitive dissonance is defined by psychologists as a condition of conflict or anxiety resulting from inconsistency between one's beliefs and one's actions. A prime example from our culture is knowing about the dangers of driving while distracted—whether from texting, checking social media, or just talking on a cell phone—but doing it anyway. Greenfield notes that, if our brain were to ask, "How important is this text? Is it worth killing somebody for?" we of course would say, "No." But because of the influence of the dopamine, we are not as able to use good judgment, and so don't process through the potential consequences. We just react.

Texting is hazardous because it uses our visual, manual, and cognitive processes, and thus takes our attention off what is happening on the road. We are *looking* at the phone, *using our hands* to operate the phone, and *thinking* about the messages we are receiving and sending. Any or all of these behaviors, even if they take only a few seconds, could cause us to miss a potential upcoming hazard and could result in an accident. Even if the time taken away from watching the road is just five seconds, in that time a vehicle traveling at 55 mph can go the length of a football field.

Mindfulness

> *Mindfulness means paying attention in a particular way. On purpose, in the present moment, and nonjudgmentally.*
> Jon Kabat-Zinn, Ph.D.

Mindfulness has many synonyms: awareness, attention, focus, presence, or vigilance. The opposite is not just mindlessness, but also distractedness, inattention, and lack of engagement. While meditation was originally derived from philosophies and practices associated with such faiths as Hinduism and Buddhism, today the practice of what most people know as meditation or mindfulness is *not* tied to religion. Mindfulness is less about spirituality and more about concentration: training your brain to quiet your mind, focus your attention on the present, and dismiss any distractions that come your way. Mindfulness meditation is like exercise, such as doing reps at a gym. It strengthens your ability to sustain attention by requiring you to sharpen your focus and pay attention to your breath. Brain benefits of mindfulness meditation include stress reduction, better focus and attention, greater compassion, and improved memory and creativity. Being engaged 100% does not come easily, especially in our world of distractions. You can practice mindfulness while doing any activity, such as eating, washing the dishes, or reading. Developing a habit of mindfulness takes effort but can profoundly affect your health and life. Try setting a timer to chime every hour or so to remind yourself to stop and pay attention to your breath, body, emotions, and environment.

> *If you are depressed, you are living in the past. If you are anxious, you are living in the future. If you are content, you are living in the present.*
> Kate Sciandra

Orienting to Your Breathing Practice

1. Close your eyes, relax, and *focus on your breathing*. As thoughts and emotions enter your mind, be aware of them, but continue to focus on your breathing.
2. Breathe normally, gradually letting your breathing slow down until it is quiet, even, and the lengths of the breaths are fairly long. Be conscious of everything that is happening in yourself.
3. If following your breath seems difficult, count your breaths. As you breathe in and out, count one in your mind. For the second breath, count two. Continue through five. This counting helps your mind to focus on your breath.

Mindfulness Sleep-Induction Technique

When in bed, you can practice mindfulness breathing to help you fall asleep.

1. Begin with abdominal breathing: place one hand on your chest and one on your abdomen, breathing in so that the hand on your abdomen rises higher than the hand on your chest.
2. Take a slow, deep breath in through your nose for a count of 1-4, then exhale slowly through your mouth for a count of 5-8.
3. Allow your thoughts to focus on your breath and the air gently entering and leaving your nose and mouth. Repeat this cycle until you fall asleep or at least feel like you will.

Chapter Seven
Speed of Processing and Fluency

Review of Chapter Six
1. What does it mean to say that *attention* functions like a spotlight? (p. 75)
2. Explain what is meant by the statement that *multitasking* is a myth. (p. 76)
3. Describe what is meant by *mindfulness* and identify some of its benefits. (p. 85)

In this chapter you will learn about and engage in exercises to improve *processing speed,* which refers to how quickly your brain can hold and manipulate information (thinking speed), and *fluency* which, with respect to cognitive function, refers to how easily you are able to retrieve words and information from memory.

How many of each kind of animal did God tell Moses to bring onto the ark?

What is your answer? If it is *two,* reread the question, paying close attention to the words. The question asks about Moses, not Noah. If you answered two, you may need to slow your brain in order to better process the incoming information to arrive at the correct answer.

A lily on a pond doubles in size each day, completely covering the surface of the pond by day 20. On what day would this lily cover half of the pond's surface?

What is your answer? About 50 percent of people say day 10. The correct answer is day 19, because the lily doubles in size each day. If it totally covers the pond's surface on day 20, then it would cover half of the pond on day 19. Arriving at the correct number requires you to slow down your brain to give it the time it needs to focus on the specifics, which in this case is working backwards to determine the answer.

Speed of Processing

The brain requires time to process information and plan an appropriate response. This "thinking" time is known as processing speed and determines how effectively you can react to and remember events. It is also closely associated with attention and can impact such daily activities as following a conversation, remembering what you have heard or read, making decisions quickly, and reacting to surprises or danger (such as when driving a car).

One consequence of normal age-related brain deterioration is slower processing, which makes it more difficult to encode, process, and respond to information. The brain's ability to efficiently process information is also affected by *fatigue* and *reduced sensory input* due to hearing loss or poor vision. People with slower information processing will take longer to respond to questions and complete tasks. They may lose track of information and task requirements and may not be able to process complex information adequately—for example, when following conversations or lengthy instructions.

Timothy Salthouse, the leading theorist in speed of processing among elders, said aging itself is moderately related to slowed cognition (Salthouse, 2000). Additional contributors are health status, general life experiences and previous practice with similar tasks, as well as the nature of the tasks themselves.

Word Fluency Exercise Using Letters and Categories as Retrieval Cues

Think of and write an appropriate word for each section in the grid below. For example, if the letter provided for a city or state was **S**, some possible answers would be Seattle, Scottsdale, South Dakota, or South Carolina.

	City or State	Food	Animal	Vehicle (make or model)
T				
E				
A				
M				
	Boys' names	Things to wear	Girls' names	Color
B				
P				
G				
S				

Name that Thing Exercise (See Answer #15, page 140)

For each category and letter below, say or write a word that fits. See how quickly you can complete each list.

Name an animal that **begins** with letter   C   _____

A fish   S   _____

A bird   E   _____

A vegetable	P	_____
A profession	D	_____
An article of clothing	T	_____
A country	I	_____
A city	N	_____
A state	A	_____
A planet	M	_____

The brain has a *lexicon*, or mental dictionary, which organizes words by first letter as in an external dictionary. This is why retrieving a word by its last letter is more challenging than retrieving a word by its first letter.

Name an animal that **ends** with letter	E	_____
A fish	A	_____
A bird	W	_____
A vegetable	H	_____
A profession	Y	_____
An article of clothing	T	_____
A country	D	_____
A city	O	_____
A state	S	_____
A planet	H	_____

Find Words Ending in ...ration (See Answer #16, page 141)

For each the following exercises, read the definition and try to think of a word with the ending provided. An example is given for each.

Of homage	*adoration*
Surgery	_____
A party or fete	_____
Deliverance	_____
Of kindness	_____
A pardoning	_____
Tuning adjustment	_____
Company	_____

Find Words Ending in...ace (See Answer #17, page 141)

The ace which supports	*brace*
A small quantity	_____
Fine open fabric	_____
Unoccupied area	_____
A competition	_____
A rate of speed	_____
Dishonor	_____
Obliterate	_____
A visage	_____
Lose something	_____
To clasp	_____
Elegance	_____

Find Words Ending in...age (See Answer #18, page 142)

The age which binds	*bandage*
Someone wise	_____
Of the theater	_____
Bravery	_____
Captive	_____
Part of a book	_____
To betroth	_____
Of intense anger	_____
Of leaves	_____
Of matrimony	_____

Find Words Ending in ...ice (See Answer #19, page 142)

Cost of something	*price*
Liquid from fruit	
Option or selection	
Guidance	
Lack of bravery	
Lack of fairness	
Ill will, evil intention	
Preconceived opinion	
Crime conspirator	
Student learning trade	

Find Words Ending in ...ise (See Answer #20, page 142)

Thoughtfully plan/invent	*devise*
Ideal/idyllic place	
Promote product/service/event	
Rebuke/reprimand severely	
Cut foreskin off	
Activity to improve fitness	
Create/perform spontaneously	
Direct execution of task/project	
Goods to be bought and sold	
Way to settle a dispute	

Find Words Ending in ...ight (See Answer #21, page 143)

Impressive power/strength	*might*
Heaviness of person/thing	
Plant disease	
Measurement from base to top	
Right of possession from birth	
Great pleasure	
Movement through air	
Ability to see	
Extending in one direction	
Understanding situation after	

Find Words Ending in …ury (See Answer #22, page 143)

Put or hide under ground	*bury* _____
State of extravagance	_____
Telling a lie under oath	_____
Heavy silvery-white metal	_____
Revenue/funds of government	_____
Hurt or damage	_____
Charging unreasonable interest	_____
Period of one hundred years	_____
Wild or violent anger	_____
Indigence, extreme poverty	_____

Phonological and Semantic Fluency Practice

- In one minute, name as many words (no proper names) as you can that begin with a randomly selected letter from the alphabet; then try again with a different alphabet letter.

- Write six or more things that begin with the letter "s" that you can wear on your feet. **(See Answer #23, page 143)**

_____

- Name *two objects* for every letter in your complete name. Work up to *five* objects, trying to use different objects each time.

- From *A* to *Z*, how many articles of *clothing* can you name in two minutes? (Try to name at least one clothing item for each letter of the alphabet.)

- In one minute, name as many *fruits* as you can. Do the same for *verbs*.

- Say the days of the week *backwards*, then in *alphabetical order.* This activity requires *executive functioning* resources, or the ability to *attend* to the task and to *inhibit* putting this information in its usual order. Time how long it takes to say these lists backwards or alphabetized and try to beat your best scores. Then try to do the same with the months.

Word Forming Activity

From a given word, see *how many words* of *three or more letters* you can form from it in *five minutes*. Or, work on it a little a day, and see if you can think of more words each day. You may use the letters more than once to create the different words, but each word created may not have more of each letter than is in the original word (i.e., if the original word has only one *b*, each of your words may contain only one *b*). Some possible words to use for this exercise: *bequeath, introduce, unmovable, scoreboard, generation, vegetation, camaraderie, readability*

Speed Card Matching

From a deck of playing cards, put *one* of each card from Ace – King *face up* in a row. Shuffle the rest and put the pile face down on the table. Pick up the top card and lay it on the card with the same number (e.g., put a 6 over a 6), repeating until the deck is exhausted. Time yourself, then do it again, trying to beat your time.

Mathematical Fluency

Find the sum of your date of birth, mm/dd/yyyy, in two ways:

1. Add each individual digit: _____

2. Add the numbers that represent the month, the date, and the year:

_____

For example, adding each digit of a birthdate of 04/13/1942 would result in a sum of 24, while adding the month, date, year would give a sum of 1959. Do the same with friends' and relatives' dates of birth.

Manual Speed of Processing Practice

Make a fist with both hands. Then, put out the pointer (index) finger of your right hand, pointing to your left hand. Put your thumb up on your left hand. Try to switch hand positions so the right hand is doing what the left was doing and vice versa. Continue switching and try to do this faster and faster.

When hands must do opposite, unfamiliar tasks, the result is "bimanual interference." This explains why learning to play the piano or type on a keyboard, in which each hand is doing something different, requires practice!

Misspelled Items Grocery List Exercise (See Answer #24, page 143)

Below are foods which might be purchased at a grocery store, but each item is misspelled by one letter. Identify the correct foods in one minute by only changing one letter in each word. For example, replacing the *d* in the word *dice* with an *r* makes it *rice*. Do not change the letter *order*.

tear	_____	soap	_____	gun	_____
fork	_____	break	_____	beach	_____
steam	_____	coin	_____	dream	_____
mile	_____	lake	_____	dish	_____

Trail-Making Activity

Put your pencil or pen on number 1 below, and draw a line to the first month, January. Without taking your pen/pencil off the paper, continue to alternate between numbers and months in the correct order until your line reaches December. This exercise stimulates your brain because it requires simultaneously thinking about number and month sequences.

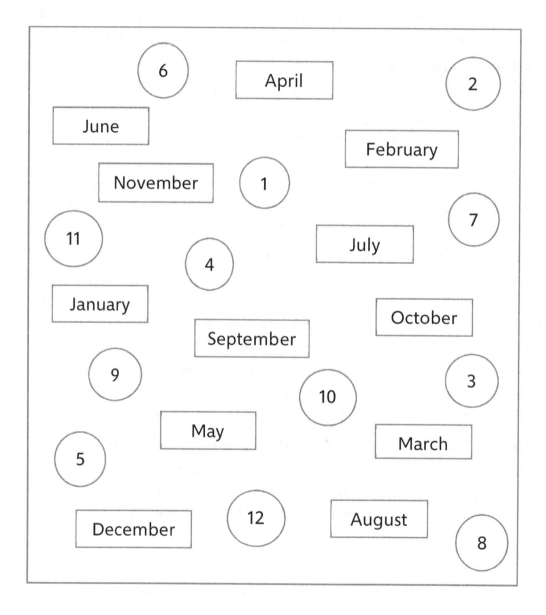

Chapter Eight
Long-term Memory for Names, Numbers, and Tasks

Review of Chapter Seven
1. In addition to aging, what other factors influence *speed of processing*? (p. 87)
2. Why is it more difficult for our brain to retrieve a word by its *last* letter than by its *first* letter? (p. 89)

In Chapter Five you learned about the information processing model of memory to better understand how memory works. You learned about the limited capacity of Short-Term Memory (STM) and the role of Working Memory (WM). In this chapter you will learn specific strategies for encoding names, numbers, and tasks in Long-Term Memory (LTM). These include the use of acronyms and acrostics, method of loci, keyword method, peg word method, and story method. This chapter also includes tips for improving prospective memory, which is remembering to do things in the future.

Brain Break
Two women were sitting on a bench. The first one said, "My memory is *so* bad," to which the other responded, "How bad is it?"
The first one replied, "How bad is what?"

The computer can serve as a metaphor for the human brain, since our brain continually engages in the processes of encoding, storing, and retrieving information. One might say something like, "There's no more room on the hard drive." The analogy breaks down, however, when we consider that if human memory *is* like a computer, everything we ever put in it should still be there. Experience tells us it is not!

Have you ever noticed that the only times we really pay attention to our memory are when it fails us? We tend to take for granted the myriad of things we remember on a daily basis: how to brush our teeth and get dressed, how to cook, the route we drive to work, names and phone numbers and other information we need to know to carry out our routines. It's when we can't recall a name or where we left our keys that we notice our memory—and either get frustrated with it or become concerned we are developing Alzheimer's disease. People younger than 50 will often attribute memory lapses to information overload, stress, or a busy and hectic lifestyle. Those over 50 will joke about "senior moments," or start worrying about dementia, especially if an older relative has been a victim of it.

> *Memory is not a passive experience but rather an active process, something you consciously choose to do.*
> Frank Felberbaum

Memory is not so much a *thing* (a storage area) as an active *process*. It involves not merely storing information in your brain but building neural connections to create pathways that didn't exist before. Memory can be considered a skill, like golf or playing piano; like any skill, you need to practice in order to improve. You can *learn* strategies for improving memory, but if you do not *practice* them, your memory will not improve. You need to develop good memory habits. As "memory magician" Harry Lorayne said, "There is no such thing as a bad memory; there are only trained and untrained memories." A trained memory can aid you in your personal life, school, and career.

Most memory strategies involve improving attention and concentration when encoding new information into memory or enhancing organization of information to ease recall and retrieval. To have a more reliable memory, you need to learn and practice strategies until you can use them effortlessly and, ideally, automatically.

Brain Break
> *Memory is what tells a man his wife's birthday was yesterday.*

General Strategies for Storing Information in LTM

- Repeat information to yourself or out loud. For example, if someone gives you directions, repeat them to the person to make sure you heard and encoded them correctly. Discuss newly learned material with a friend to reinforce it in your mind.
- The more thoroughly you *understand* new information, the greater the chance you will remember not only the general concept but also the details. Improve your *comprehension* by re-reading material, asking questions about it, and discussing it.
- When ideas occur to you, *write them down* as soon as you can, to reinforce them in your mind. Later, you may be able to recall them without looking at the notes, but at least you will have notes in case your memory does fail.

- Research on learning has shown that *spaced rehearsal* is more effective than cramming. You will remember something more effectively if you rehearse it for 15 minutes a day for four consecutive days than if you rehearse it for 60 minutes on one day. Spacing out study sessions gives your brain a chance to consolidate the information you have learned and to form a more lasting memory. Remember that information processing speed slows with age, so be patient and give yourself the time you need to absorb new information.

"Chunking" Information

Chunking is useful for remembering numbers. Phone numbers are naturally chunked into the area code, local exchange, and remaining four digits. If your checking account number is 379852654, instead of memorizing it as a string of nine single digits, try grouping the digits into three triple-digit numbers: 379, 852, and 654. This reduces the number of items you need to remember from nine to three.

Organizing Information

Would you prefer your memory to resemble your silverware drawer or your junk drawer? In which drawer is it easier to find a specific item? Picture a large cardboard box and a small file box. Suppose you put information on cards and then toss some into the large box, but file others into the small box. From which box would it take less time to retrieve a specific card? There is something to be said for organization, whether it be of physical stuff or mental stuff!

Can you recite the months of the year in 10 seconds or less? Try it. Now, recite them alphabetically in that same time limit. It is likely that you were not able to succeed. Why not? How were the months organized when you first learned and encoded them? The way in which we organize information when encoding it can influence ease of retrieval. The poorer the organization, the less efficient the retrieval.

There are numerous and varied ways to organize information. For example, you can group things categorically, chronologically, numerically, or alphabetically. You can create lists or outlines or put the information into graphic organizers or "trees," grouping together similar facts or principles. Finding a way to "chunk" information in these ways reduces the load on memory. *Information that is well organized is much easier to learn and remember.*

External Aids

You can also use *external aids*, such as address books, calendars, to-do lists, post-it note reminders, timers, and other devices to record information, appointments, and tasks. Develop a habit of consistently recording information with external aids and of consulting the aids regularly.

- **Keys, glasses, wallet or purse, and other often-used items** should have designated "parking" spots in your home or car and should be placed there when you are not using them. Look intentionally at the place where you are setting an object down, and perhaps say out loud or write down the location.
- **Appointments, meetings, tasks, and important dates** (birthdays, anniversaries, etc.) should be recorded on a paper calendar or an electronic device (such as a smart phone or your computer's Google Calendar) which you check frequently each day.
- Record **contact information** (phone numbers and email addresses) of friends, relatives, and professionals and/or companies with whom you do business in your smart phone, computer, or a binder with tabs to identify categories.
- **Important documents** (insurance papers, medical records, financial statements, deeds, etc.) should be kept in a file cabinet, safe deposit box, or other designated location. If possible, scan these into a computer to make electronic records of them, so you don't have to recall their physical location.
- **Post checklists of procedures** that you may have difficulty remembering from one time to the next (e.g., using a digital camera, programming your DVR, or performing certain functions on your computer).

Do. Or do not. There is no try.
Yoda

Organizing and Categorizing to Help Memory

A list of 12 items can be organized into three groups of four related items. For example, when you plan your grocery list, think of the items you need by categories, such as dairy, produce, meats, frozen foods, and so on.

Rearrange the following grocery items into *three categories* of *four items each*, writing them on the blank lines. **Then memorize the list.**

popsicles	yogurt
ground beef	ice cream
eggs	butter
bacon	frozen corn
milk	pork roast
chicken	toaster waffles

Category name: _____

Items:_____   _____   _____   _____

Category name: _____

Items:_____   _____   _____   _____

Category name: _____

Items:_____   _____   _____   _____

> *Problems of retention must be solved primarily by finding ways of organizing information in memory so that it can be accessed efficiently when needed.*
> W. K. Estes

Mnemonics

Mnemonics (nee-MON-iks) are systematic techniques to aid memory. They take a bit of effort to learn, but the time investment can pay off when you use them to help you remember names, numbers, tasks, and other information. The word "mnemonic" comes from the name of the Greek goddess Mnemosyne, who named all the objects of the earth. Memory systems were used extensively in early Greek civilization because there was no system for writing things down. Our highly technological society has lessened the need for memory systems today. Most landline phones have a "redial" feature so you can call a second time without having to remember the number, and smart phones remember numbers so we don't have to. Most smart phones have access to the Internet, a source of almost all the information we might ever need. We can also put programs and apps on our computers and smart phones to remember all our passwords.

However, if we wish to store information in our brain, mnemonic devices can aid with storage and retrieval of information from LTM. They generally involve associating (A), visualizing (V), and/or elaborating (E) on the information. Exercises to learn and practice these strategies can be found later in this chapter.

Brain Break
One way to improve your memory is to loan people money.

PAVE Your Way to a Better Memory

PAVE is an acronym I created to help remember four tips for improving memory.

  P – pay attention
  A – associate
  V – visualize
  E – elaborate

Pay attention

From all the information coming to your brain through your senses, consciously select what you need to remember, and focus or concentrate on it. What you *pay attention* to is what enters Working Memory for further processing and possible encoding into Long-Term Memory.

Associate

Connect to-be-remembered information to something you already know. Related information automatically accesses, activates, or primes related information (e.g., "apple" is strongly connected to "red" and "fruit"). Effective associations involve similar sounds or rhymes (pool—cool), similar meanings (pupil—student), cause and effect (lightning—thunder), whole and part (yolk—egg), opposites and contrasts (black—white, hot—cold), pairs associated by tradition (bacon—eggs, horse—carriage), or acronyms (using the first letter of each to-be-remembered item to create a word or phrase).

> *You can remember any new piece of information if it is associated to something you already know or remember.*
> Harry Lorayne

Acronyms

An acronym is a word or group of letters where each letter represents the first letter in a word or response you're trying to remember. In the world of texting, acronyms have become basic vocabulary (e.g. LOL for "laughing out loud"). And even before the days of texting, many acronyms were used as a shorthand method of communicating expressions, names of organizations, etc. When I lived in Boulder, Colorado, I worked for a company called NBI. I never did find out what those initials stood for, but joked that it meant, "Nothing But Initials." Another company in the area was IBM. When asked what that stood for, its employees often replied, "I've Been Moved," because they had been transferred around the country from one IBM location to another.

Common Acronyms
ASAP – as soon as possible
AWOL – absent without leave
SASE– self-addressed stamped envelope
SCUBA – self-contained underwater breathing apparatus
SNAFU – situation normal all fouled up

Acronyms can serve as a short cut for memory. They bring up the initial letters of a phrase or series of words we wish to recall, and help our brain zoom right to their associates. Have you ever met ROY G BIV? This is not a person but represents an acronym for the colors of the visible spectrum (rainbow), in order (red, orange, yellow, green, blue, indigo, violet). If you live in the Midwest, you may be familiar with HOMES. It is often easy to recall some of the Great Lakes, but not all five. With this acronym, you can whiz through the list: Huron, Ontario, Michigan, Erie, Superior. In a business environment, when helping employees set goals or objectives, managers often use the acronym SMART: specific, measurable, appropriate, reasonable, and timely.

FAST

Acronym from the National Stroke Association to help determine when a person needs to obtain immediate medical help:

F = Face – Ask the person to smile. Does one side of the face droop?

A = Arms – Ask the person to raise both arms. Does one arm drift downward?

S = Speech – Ask the person to repeat a sentence. Does it sound slurred or jumbled?

T = Time – If you see any of these signs, call 9-1-1 or get to the nearest stroke center.

Creating acronyms can assist with memory in daily life as well as on the job. If while driving you think of some tasks you need to complete when you get home, you might create an acronym using the first letter of each task. For example, if you need to add windshield washer fluid to your car, make a hotel reservation for an upcoming trip, invite a new neighbor to lunch, and wrap a gift to take to a friend's birthday party, you can coin the acronym WHIG, where each letter represents one of the four tasks. Once home, recalling the acronym can lead to decoding it to recall the four tasks: Windshield wiper, Hotel reservation, Invitation, Gift.

A woman at one of my speaking engagements told me she always thinks about ST. MIKE before leaving the house: Sunglasses, Telephone, Medications, ID, Keys, and Ears (hearing aids)!

Acrostics

Acrostics are phrases or complete sentences in which the first letters of the words represent letters that are also the first letters of the words or information you are trying to remember. For example:

- Every Good Boy Does Fine for EGBDF (in music, the lines of the treble clef)
- Never Eat Soggy Waffles (or Never Eat Shredded Wheat) for the directions on a compass (North, East, South, and West, in clockwise order)

- My Very Educated Mother Just Served Us Noodles (the eight planets in order from the sun: Mercury, Venus, Earth, Mars, Jupiter, Saturn, Uranus, Neptune)
- A Rat in the House Might Eat the Ice Cream (spelling of arithmetic)
- Please Excuse My Dear Aunt Sally (the order of operations in math: Parentheses, Exponent, Multiply, Divide, Add, Subtract)

Visualize

Form mental pictures of to-be-remembered information. For example, if you park your car in space 5 of level C at the mall, visualize 5 cats waiting in your car for your return. To remember that Augusta is the capital of Maine, picture a gust of wind blowing through a horse's mane.

For effective imagery:
- Pick out the most important aspects of the material you want to remember.
- Make your image concrete – something you can see, hear, smell, taste and/or feel. Use as many senses as you can.
- **ACE** your images – use **a**ction, **c**olor and **e**xaggeration.

Keyword Method

The keyword method can be used to learn vocabulary, either in your language or a foreign language. It involves making associations between the new word and definition you are trying to learn using a sound-alike word which can easily be visualized.

- Create a sound-alike proxy (keyword) for a new vocabulary word, proper name, fact or concept.
- Through an interactive picture or image, link the keyword to the word you're trying to learn.
- Examples: To remember that the word *duct* means *pipe*, use the word *duck* (keyword) as a sound-alike, and then form an interactive image of a duck *in* a pipe. *Ranid* refers to the family of typical frogs, so visualize a picture of a frog sitting in the *rain* (keyword). To remember that the Spanish word *burro* means *butter*, visualize a burro covered in butter. To remember that the French word *haricot* means *bean*, visualize a bean wearing a hairy coat.

Method of Loci

This is a mnemonic device that relies on spatial relationships between "loci" (locations on a familiar route or rooms in a familiar building called a "memory palace") to store and then recall information. The origin of this ancient method is attributed to the Greek poet Simonides and its effectiveness is reflected in its continued use over more than two millennia in a virtually unchanged form.

The first step is to think of a set of familiar locations you can easily visualize, such as your front door, hall closet, sofa in living room, etc. When you have a list of words/objects to memorize, you visualize each of them in one of the locations. As an example, say you need to recall three points for a presentation at a meeting: personnel issues, new software, and budget issues. You could visualize many people going through your front door (personnel), a computer in your hall closet (software), and a bushel of thousand-dollar bills on the sofa (budget).

Method of Loci Exercise

Visualize walking through your house and select five locations where you could put something. For example, you could put something on the couch in the living room, on top of the TV set, on the kitchen counter, on your bed, and so on.

Memorize your list of five locations in order. Then, study the words in the list below and try to visualize *each* object in *one* of the locations you picked earlier. For instance, if one of the words was "duck," and one of your locations was "bathtub," you could visualize a duck floating in your bathtub. The sillier the image, the more likely you are to remember it. Do the same for each subsequent item on the list. Then imagine yourself walking from one location to another in your house, seeing the items you've imagined.

1. paint brush
2. stamps
3. potting soil
4. rake
5. cotton balls

Later, without looking at the list, visualize your locations and see if you can recall the items.

Elaborate

> *We soon forget what we have not deeply thought about.*
> Marcel Proust

Elaboration is a strategy which involves processing information to a deeper level by thinking about it in a meaningful way. In a classic experiment, people who thought about the *meaning* of a word for each word in a list recalled more words than those who only thought about a *rhyming* word (Craik & Tulving, 1975).

- Try to find ways to connect the to-be-remembered (TBR) information meaningfully with something *already in* long-term memory.
- Create a verbal connection between what you are trying to remember and something associated with it. For *laggard*, meaning slow and sluggish, say:

"Having jet lag can make you feel slow and sluggish." To remember that Juneau is the capital of Alaska, use the question, "D'you know (*pronounce like Juneau*) the capital of Alaska?"

- Use *organization* to categorize or alphabetize the to-be-remembered items.
- Create a *story* to connect the to-be-remembered items, converting abstract words into related words that can be easily pictured.

Brain Break (See Answer #25, page 144) *Can you match the "punny" ending to the proper beginning?*

1. I couldn't remember how to throw a boomerang ____
2. I used to do rock climbing as a youth ____
3. Tennis players seldom marry because ____
4. Archery contests are usually won ____
5. Marathon runners with bad footwear ____
6. The scuba diving student was ____

a) but I was much boulder back then.
b) suffer the agony of de feet.
c) by an arrow margin.
d) in over his head.
e) love means nothing to them.
f) but then it came back to me.

Spelling Elaboration Exercise (See Answer #26, page 144)

Correct spelling can be remembered by creating phrases or sentences which cue the correct letters in that part of the word in which errors are likely to be made.

Write phrases or sentences to help you recall the spelling of the words below. Some examples are provided.

already	
believe	Never beLIEve a LIE.
chauffeur	Our chauffEUR hates the traffic in EURope.
forty	
inoculation	
outrageous	
parallel	Draw ALL the lines parALLel.
plague	
principal	The princiPAL is your PAL.
stationery	

Vocabulary Elaboration Exercise (See Answer #27, page 144)

Elaboration can be used to help remember definitions of words. For example, for *gregarious*, which means *outgoing and social,* you could elaborate by saying "Gregory is a friendly guy," since the name *Gregory* sounds like *gregarious,* and *friendly* fits the definition of that word.

For each word below, write a sentence to help you remember its definition.

aberrant (to stray from the right or usual course)	
altruism (unselfish concern for others)	
delta (land at the mouth of a river)	
truculent (fierce, cruel, savagely brutal)	
winsome (sweetly or innocently charming, engaging)	

States and Capitals Elaboration Exercise (See Answer #28, page 145)

Create phrases, sentences, and/or images that incorporate the name of the capital and the state. Two examples are provided.

Little Rock, Arkansas	
Tallahassee, Florida	
Augusta, Maine	*A gust of* wind blew through my horse's *mane.*
Helena, Montana	A girl named *Helena* is climbing a *mountain.*
Harrisburg, Pennsylvania	
Cheyenne, Wyoming	

Story Elaboration Exercise (See Answer #29, page 145)

Create a story that uses the words in the following list (the first 13 states):

Delaware, Pennsylvania, New Jersey, Georgia, Connecticut, Massachusetts, Maryland, South Carolina, New Hampshire, Virginia, New York, North Carolina, Rhode Island

Peg Word Elaboration Method and Practice

This method is best used for remembering ordered information, such as items in a series (the Presidents, the first 10 Amendments to the Constitution, or the causes of the Civil War). It is a rhyming system involving numbers that uses a predetermined list of "pegs" on which to hang, or place, information that is to be remembered. You can use any words for your pegs if they are easy to picture in your mind and rhyme with their associated number. One possible list of peg words follows:

1 = bun	2 = shoe	3 = tree	4 = door	5 = hive
6 = sticks	7 = heaven	8 = gate	9 = wine	10 = hen

The goal is to form a mental image of the *peg word* interacting with the numbered item. For example, if the first task on your "to-do" list is to buy stamps at the post office, visualize a bun covered with postage stamps.

Find a list of the first 10 Presidents, the Bill of Rights, the Ten Commandments, or another list of 10 items you can try to memorize using the peg word method.

For example, the Second Amendment is the right to bear arms. Since the image for 2 is shoe, you could create an image of a shoe with a gun in it. In some Bibles the eighth commandment is, "Thou shalt not steal." Since the image for 8 is gate, you could picture someone climbing over a gate to steal from someone's back yard.

Elaboration and Practice for Remembering Numbers

Many, but not all, people find it more difficult to remember numbers than words or verbal information, possibly because numbers are often arbitrary and have no semantic (meaningful) connection with other information. The phonetic consonant alphabet system is one method for memorizing numbers. However, it is a complicated system to learn and, unless one has to memorize many numbers, most people would not want to invest the time to master it. Following are some other techniques which can help with everyday tasks that require memorizing numbers.

Chunk – Try to *divide*, or recode, a long number into chunks (groups of digits)

Analyze the number mathematically – Try to identify *mathematical relationships* between the numbers (e.g., 369-3729 is multiples of 3 followed by two prime numbers 37 and 29)

Visualize the number – Pause and take a *mental picture*; visualize the number in bright red against a white wall, or in yellow neon against a dark sky

Recode phone numbers using the letters on the keypad – If phone keypad letters are associated with each digit, try to form a word or phrase (843-5464 is THE KING, 439-5466 is HEY LION)

Create a phrase – Think of a phrase in which the number of letters in each word represents one of the digits in the number (an ATM PIN could be 1425 for "I want my money")

Use common associations – Use words and images associated with certain numbers (eggs for 12, speed limit sign for 55), units of time (12:15), dates (holidays, such as 1225, historical years, such as 1492, or friends' birthdates), or measurements (5280, the number of feet in a mile); for example, if some friends' address is 1225 Chestnut St., visualize a decorated Christmas tree on their roof and "see" them roasting chestnuts in their fireplace

Use elaboration to convert the number to a memorable phrase – For example, if Carey's license plate is BC1216 and his birthday is December 16, it can be converted to Born Carey 12/16

Select a number from the three options below, think of *strategies* you could use to *memorize* the number, then attempt to commit it memory:

- Your new library access number is 839208490
- Your granddaughter's new phone number is 617-745-4977
- Your own license plate number, driver's license number, or other long number you wish to have in your memory.

Think about how you would use *association, visualization, and/or elaboration* to remember the following name and address:

Paul Edwards
The Pines, #3
57 Forest Lane
Paducah, KY 42001

Prospective Memory

Retrospective memory (remembering the past) involves *content* or *information*. *Prospective memory*, on the other hand, is one of the most practical aspects of memory, and involves *remembering to do things at the appropriate time*, such as taking medication, calling loved ones on their birthdays, mailing checks to pay bills, etc. The key to *prospective memory* is to create a *cue* for yourself so you can retrieve the memory at the proper time.

For example, you might *wear your watch or a ring on the opposite hand* from the one on which you normally wear it and *tell yourself* that this is *to remind you* to do something (like make a doctor appointment) later. While hairdressers rarely send an email or text to remind us of upcoming appointments, dentists usually do, since we generally remember things that are more appealing to do than things that are not!

Prospective Memory Exercise (See Answer #30, page 145)

For each task below, think of strategies to help you remember to do them at the correct time. Some possible strategies are in the **Answers to Exercises** chapter.

1. On Sunday night return Susan's book to her at dinner.
2. In ten days, mail a birthday card to George.
3. Meet Harry and Gladys for lunch at the Bistro tomorrow at 12:30.
4. Schedule your next doctor appointment.

Remembering to Take Medication

Brain Break

A man phoned his doctor's office and anxiously asked, "Is it true that the medication you prescribed has to be taken for the rest of my life?"

"Yes, I'm afraid so," the doctor told him. There was a moment of silence before the man replied, "I'm wondering, then, just how serious my condition is, because this prescription is marked 'NO REFILLS'!"

Poor cognition is associated with both over and under adherence to a prescribed medication regimen. Forgetting is a major reason medication doses are missed, but overconsumption also happens, especially with people on a once-daily dose schedule. That is why it is important to use strategies to help remember to take medication in the appropriate amounts and at the appropriate times, and to keep track of when you've taken it.

Sometimes medication doses are missed because it is easy to confuse *thinking* about taking your medication with *doing* it, since the same brain regions are activated for both. So, your brain may "remember" taking it when you only *thought about* doing so. Also, with repeated activities, the numerous memories we have of the task can blur together.

Tips for correct medication consumption:

- Keep medication visible: leave it out in an easy-to-spot place.
- Associate taking medications with meals or daily routines, like brushing your teeth, making coffee, reading the morning newspaper, or watching the evening news.
- Put your medications in pillboxes, such as the simple seven-day plastic pillbox or a decorative one. There are also pillboxes with technology that buzz or use an electronic voice to remind you to take your medications. Some even dispense the medicine at the appropriate times.
- Keep a chart, calendar, or even a sticky note in a place you see every day, as long as you remember to look at it.
- Set alarms on watches or smart phones or use online calendar services. For example, Google Calendar can help organize your life by sending reminders, such as when to take your medication, to your smart phone. And it is free.

Remembering a Doctor's Instructions Practice

Read the instructions below, then cover them and say them from memory.

1. *I'm writing you a prescription for erythromycin. You will need to take two a day, one in the morning and one in the evening, with food, for five days.*
2. *Buy some Sinutabs for your congestion and take two Sinutabs every six hours for a week, or as long as the congestion lasts.*
3. *Drink lots of fluids. If your fever is not gone within 48 hours, call me again.*

Organizing and Categorizing Grocery List Recall Exercise (See Answer #31, page 145)

A few pages back you categorized and memorized a grocery list. Write the category and item names below. Did categorizing them help you remember?

Category name: _____

Items:_____ _____ _____ _____

Category name: _____

Items:_____ _____ _____ _____

Category name: _____

Items:_____ _____ _____ _____

Everyday Memory Exercises (See Answer #32, page 146)

Use memory strategies you have learned in this book for these challenges:

1. Suppose you wish to remember to buy these eight things at the store:

toilet paper	*carrots*	*crackers*	*frozen pizza*
laundry detergent	*corn flakes*	*lettuce*	*cat food*

   a. Make up a *story* that includes all the items. (You may rearrange the order if that helps.)

   b. Use the *method of loci* to visualize each item on the list in one of the places in your house or in one of a series of familiar locations.

2. You and your friends are seated at a table in a restaurant. The waitress comes and introduces herself. How can you remember her name and what she looks like when you need her later? (Assume that she is not wearing a name tag.)

3. You are taking some visiting relatives to an amusement park. How would you remember to show them all the important (fun) areas?

4. You are sitting with some friends who are telling jokes. You hear a couple that you really like and want to be able to tell them to others. How do you remember them?

5. What can you do to memorize the following announcements you need to make to the members of your book club when it meets next week?

   Pot luck supper is on October 15

   Bring two old books to donate

   Coffee will cost $1.00 starting next month

   On your way out, please take an invitation to give to a friend

6. How will you remember to do these five errands tomorrow (not necessarily in this order)?

   Visit an acquaintance in the hospital

   Take your suit to the cleaners

   Buy a birthday present for your grandson

   Pick up your new glasses at the optometrist's office

   Get stamps at the post office

7. A new acquaintance gives you his phone number, which is 10 digits with the area code. You have no means with which to write it down. What could you do to try to remember it?

> *I like nonsense. It wakes up the brain cells.*
> Dr. Seuss

Visual Recall Practice

Study the objects in the following image for one minute and try to memorize the nine items in any order. When the minute is up, cover the picture, multiply 9 x 47, and then write the names of the items in any order. This exercise is different from the one in Chapter Five because the time to do the multiplication problem requires you to remember the items for more than 20-30 seconds, so it is more of a long-term memory exercise, since that exceeds the duration of short-term memory.

Remembering Names

Do you have difficulty remembering names? Most people I meet say they do. Why is that? Think about it: first, we probably do not pay enough attention when a name is said. If we are thinking about anything else during that moment, the name will not be encoded. Also, there are so many names to remember! Many are difficult to pronounce or spell. And sometimes we know we will never see the person again, so our brain has little motivation to learn the name.

Have you ever seen someone coming toward you, and you recognize the person's face, but cannot recall the associated name? The face is an image, and our brain generally has more success with remembering images than verbal information. In addition, seeing a familiar face involves recognition, while remembering the name involves recall, and recognition entails less mental effort than recall. Think back to when you had to take multiple choice tests in school, which involved merely picking the correct answer from the options presented, versus writing an essay, which required you to come up with all the information.

Have you ever had a parent call you by your sibling's name, or have you ever called one of your children the name of his or her sibling? In a memorable episode of the sitcom *Friends,* at the altar Ross utters the name of his previous girlfriend instead of the name of the woman he is about to marry! Since information in LTM is connected in a mental semantic network, thinking about one concept, person, or place sends activation to related concepts, and through a process called "priming" may cause us to say a related word instead of the one we intended. Researchers asked more than 1,700 people whether they had ever been misnamed or if they had ever committed a misnaming (Deffler, 2016). Their results confirmed that these errors are common, committed by people of all ages, and do not appear to be an indicator of aging or of the cognitive decline typically associated with Alzheimer's disease.

Context Effect

Have you ever walked into a room and, once there, been unable to recall why you went into that room?

Another reason remembering names can be challenging is that memory is *context* dependent; what we learn or encode in one environment or setting is more difficult to retrieve in a different place. Have you ever met people at work, school or church, and then run into them in a grocery store or the mall and been unable to remember their names? This could be attributed to the change in context.

In a classic experiment, scuba divers learned lists of words in two natural environments: on dry land and underwater (Godden & Baddeley, 1975). They then recalled the words in either the environment in which they learned them or the alternate one. Recall was best when it was performed in the same environment in which the words were learned. This study, done outside of the lab and in the real world, supported the phenomenon of context-dependent memory.

If you encounter someone but can't recall his/her name:

1. Think about the *context* in which you last saw the person (place, time of year, event) to see if that helps you retrieve the name.

2. Do a quick alphabetic search of names until you *recognize* the name (Anne, Amy, Betty, Barbara, Carol, etc.)

3. Admit you can't recall the person's name. Chances are that the person may admit he/she cannot recall your name, either!

Strategies for Remembering Names

> **Brain Break**
>
> A woman was introduced to a couple at a community luncheon. She decided to remember their names by noting they were the same as those of two characters in a popular children's story. When the couple was leaving, she teased, "Be careful going up that hill! But you must get that all the time." They smiled politely but said nothing. After they left, her husband asked, "What was that all about?" "Jack and Jill. Up the hill. Remember?" she said. "Yes, but what does that have to do with," he pointed to the couple, "Dick and Jane?"

Below are strategies which, if used regularly, will be helpful for remembering names.

- Pay **attention**: focus on the person's face and listen carefully. We need to **pay attention** to get information from *Sensory Memory* to *Short-term Memory* for further processing.
- Unless the person is wearing a name tag, or his/her name is easy to spell (like Tom Jones), *ask* for the **spelling** and **visualize** the name in writing.
- **Repeat** the name to yourself *silently* while looking at the person's face and use it *out loud* in conversation.
- Note spontaneous **associations** to the name (for John, it could be a friend named John, John Lennon, the apostle John, John Kennedy; for Campbell, soup; for Mike, a microphone; for Keith, keys). Certain first names, such as Rose, Frank, and Penny, immediately bring to mind images (flower, hot dog, coin). Last names can do the same, such as Hammer, Paige, Baker, Bush, or Horne.
- Break a longer name into **syllables** (for "Lockerty" picture a locker full of tea bags, for "Laskowski" a cow that has lost its skis, for "Rosenberg" a rose encased in an iceberg).
- Look for a **distinctive feature** or one that grabs your attention. Examine eyes, nose, lips, mouth, teeth, chin, cheekbones, forehead, ears, face shape, hair, mustache, beard, neck, birthmark, glasses, clothing, hat, jewelry.
- **Exaggerate** the feature (much as a caricaturist would do). If Shirley Castle has curly hair, see tiny castles in the curls.
- Create a mental **image** associating the name with the distinctive feature.
  - ➤ For Bill, visualize a dollar bill on his forehead.
  - ➤ If Mr. Ball has red hair, picture hundreds of red balls coming out of his hair.
  - ➤ For a wide-mouthed man named Shawn, visualize him yawning.
  - ➤ If Mr. Longino has a long face, focus on that to help recall his name.

- Use **alliteration**: select a prominent feature that has the same first letter as the name (*tall Tom, moustache Mike, round-faced Rose, long-haired Larry*)
- Use **rhyme**: think of an adjective that rhymes with the name (*Curly Shirley*, if she has curly hair; *Chain Jane* if you visualized a chain in Jane's hair; if Rachel has very smooth skin, think *facial*).
- Soon after, **write** names and descriptions of people you have just met, and **review** them before you attend an event or are somewhere you may again encounter those individuals.

A person who attended one of the author's talks said he remembered her name by picturing on her head a piece of *lint* (for Linda) on a *saucer* (for Sasser)!

Face – Name Practice

Look at the picture of Robert Pienkowski. You could focus on his blue eyes and think, "robin's egg blue," associating *Robert* with "robin." Break his last name into syllables - "pink-house-key." Visualize a *robin* perched on his head with a *pink house key* in its beak. Focus intently on this in your mind's eye, so when you next see him, his blue eyes cause you to recall the robin with the pink house key on his head, and his name.

Then, look at the photo of Shalini Patel. Shalini sounds a bit like "shawl," so picture her head covered with a shawl. For her last name, Patel, you could visualize flower "petals" on the shawl, or her "patting" the shawl to make sure it is on her head securely.

Robert Pienkowski   Shalini Patel

Study the faces and names that follow and try to think of images or associations to help remember them. Some facial features to focus on include: head shape, distinguishing marks (scars, dimples), eye and hair color, facial hair, nose, lips, ears, teeth, skin. It is the process of *elaborating* on the names, in attempting to think of images and associations, that helps *encode* the faces and names in memory.

Creating mnemonics using images requires practice. The more often you attempt to elaborate on names when you meet new people, the better you will get. You can also create images for names you will encounter often. Then, when you meet people with these names, connect the image with a feature of the person.

Some examples of images for common names:

Ashley = ashes	Ginger = gingerbread
Barbara = barbed wire	Kathy = cat
Bill = dollar bill	Keith = keys
Bob = bobsled	Lynn = lint
Bridget = bridge	Margaret = margarine
Chris = Christmas tree	Mike = mic (microphone)
Colin = collar	Norman = Norseman
Derek = oil derrick	Peggy = pegboard
Donald = Donald Duck	Sam = Uncle Sam
Frances = Eiffel Tower	Scott = Scott paper towels
Frank = frankfurter	Steve = sleeve
Gene = jeans	Tom = tomcat

Find more at: www.artofmemory.com/wiki/Memorizing_Names_and_Faces

Use the Strategies to Learn These Names:

Judy Hilton   Claudia Sanderson   Blake Lincoln   Drew Wood

Amy Wong   Dennis Armstrong   Estelle Parker   Jeff Stein

Seven Dwarfs Activity

Visualize the Seven Dwarfs in your home: *Grumpy* pouring a cup of coffee, *Sneezy* sniffing the pepper in the pantry, *Doc* rumbling around in the medicine cabinet, *Bashful* hiding in a closet, *Dopey* standing with one foot in the mop bucket, *Sleepy* on the sofa, and *Happy* sipping a glass of wine. Later, see if you can still name the Seven Dwarfs.

Concentration Game

Place pairs of playing cards in random order face down in a 6x6 array. With a partner, take turns turning over two cards; if they match, they may be picked up. If not, the player turns them back over. The goal is to *remember* locations of matching cards, and to win by collecting the most pairs.

Chapter Nine
Reasoning, Problem Solving, and Creativity

Review of Chapter Eight
1. How would you use the *method of loci* to remember a list of errands? (p. 102)
2. What are some *strategies* you can use to remember *numbers*? (p. 106)
3. What is the key for having good *prospective* memory? (p. 108)
4. State three things you can do to remember names of people you meet. (p. 113)
5. Can you recall the names of the people in these photos? (p. 114)

Psychologist Cattell proposed two different forms of intelligence: *fluid intelligence*, defined as the ability to solve new problems, use logic in new situations, and identify patterns; and *crystallized intelligence*, defined as the ability to retrieve and use information that has been acquired throughout a lifetime. Research shows that fluid intelligence tends to be disrupted with normal aging, while crystallized intelligence remains stable across the life span. For example, older adults are often better than young adults at defining words, answering questions that rely on general world knowledge (e.g., "Who wrote the 'Star Spangled Banner'?"), detecting spelling errors, or carrying out tasks related to their careers. The decline in fluid intelligence is more frequently seen with novel tasks, since older adults tend to maintain well-learned skills but have difficulty devising efficient strategies for unfamiliar or novel activities. For this reason, learning better problem-solving skills can help the brain stay young. This chapter will provide ideas for developing reasoning, problem solving, and creative thinking skills, and includes exercises to allow for the immediate practice of these.

Brain Break

The following quiz consists of four questions and will reveal something about your thinking ability.* Cover the answer to each question until you have answered it.

1. *How do you put a giraffe into a refrigerator?*

   Correct Answer: Open the refrigerator, put in the giraffe, and close the door. This question tests whether you tend to do simple things in an overly complicated way.

2. *How do you put an elephant into a refrigerator?*

   Did you say, "Open the refrigerator, put in the elephant, and close the refrigerator?"

   Wrong answer.

   Correct Answer: Open the refrigerator, take out the giraffe, put in the elephant and close the door. This tests your ability to think through the repercussions of your previous actions.

3. *The Lion King is hosting an Animal Conference. All the animals attend... except one. Which animal does not attend?*

   Correct Answer: The elephant, because he is in the refrigerator. You just put him in there. This tests your memory. Okay, even if you did not answer the first three questions correctly, you still have one more chance to show your true abilities.

4. *There is a river you must cross but it is used by crocodiles, and you do not have a boat. How do you manage it?*

   Correct Answer: You jump into the river and swim across. All the crocodiles are attending the Animal Conference. This tests whether you learn quickly from your mistakes.

*NOTE: This is *not* a real quiz about thinking ability; it is just for fun!

Reasoning

What does the term *reasoning* mean to you? *Reasoning* is the cognitive process by which people start with information and come to conclusions that go beyond that information. Reasoning is related to the process of *decision making* in that decisions are often the *outcome* of reasoning. Reasoning is also involved in *solving problems* and in *making inferences* while reading.

Reasoning often involves identifying a pattern or rule in order to solve the first in a series of problems and using that pattern to solve subsequent incidents. Our brain processes concrete, meaningful material differently than abstract material. If we encounter information that is not familiar or easily comprehended, the left hemisphere of our brain operates as an *interpreter*, automatically producing an explanation that may or may not be true. The following exercises involve different types of reasoning.

Continuing Patterns Exercise (Inductive Reasoning) (See Answer #33, page 147)

For each series below, identify what letters or numbers would follow:

Aabccdeef   _____

Acegi   _____

Zyxwv   _____

O, T, T, F, F, S, S,   _____

5, 8, 12, 15, 19, 22, 26,   _____

1, 2, 3, 5, 8, 13, 21, 34,   _____

18, 20, 24, 30, 38,   _____

Finding Patterns Exercise (See Answer #34, page 147)

Using the keypad on a cell phone, find words for each category that are represented by the patterns of numbers:

Things that are blue	759	53267	62326
Things that are round	2255	247253	288866
Vegetables	7327	778274	27622654
Dogs	766353	265543	32724863

Spatial Reasoning Exercises (See Answer #35, page 147)

Study the figure below and note the number of squares. How many are there?

Did you guess 16, as many people do? But what about the 2x2 and 3x3 squares? Count again.

Now, try to visualize a 3x3x3 inch cube, with all the outsides painted green. Then visualize it being cut into 27 one-inch cubes. How many cubes will have no, one, two, or three sides painted green? If this is too challenging to do mentally, try drawing a diagram to help you visualize it. Your number of cubes should total 27.

Ordering Exercise (See Answer #36, page 148)

Put the following names in order so that the *first* letter of each name *appears* in the next name (in any position). Keep CAREY as the first name on your list. Several correct orders are possible.

CAREY
WILLIAM
MADISON
LOGAN
HOWARD
EDITH
SCOTT
NICOLE

For a further brain challenge, try to create your own exercise like the one above.

Reason These Out Exercise (See Answer #37, page 148)

1. Mike is texting Nicole, but Nicole is texting Aaron. Mike is a minor, but Aaron is not. Is a minor texting an adult? A) Yes B) No C) Cannot be determined.

2. In this sequence, 4, 13, 40, 121, n, each term after the first is determined by multiplying the previous term by x and then adding y. What number is n?

You may have difficulty figuring out the next two challenges. Half of the students at Harvard who were given #3 were unable to reason it out. Once you have solved or looked at the solution to #3, tackle #4, which is analogous. You can solve #4 using the same reasoning used for #3.

3. A fancy shirt and a tie cost $55.00 in total. The shirt costs $50 more than the tie. How much does the tie cost?

4. A bat and a ball together cost $1.10. The bat costs $1.00 more than the ball. How much does the ball cost? (Notice how this is similar in format to the prior problem.)

Critical Thinking: Proverbs and Quotes – What Do They Mean?

Read a proverb, inspirational quote, or Bible verse. Use verbal reasoning to think about what it means to you and put it in your own words. There are no right or wrong answers; the objective is to think critically about the statement and determine your personal interpretation of it.

1. A man who dares to waste one hour of time has not discovered the value of life.
   Charles Robert Darwin
2. Our life always expresses the result of our dominant thoughts.
   Søren Aabye Kierkegaard
3. Life consists not in holding good cards but in playing those you hold well.
   Henry Wheeler Shaw (better known under his pen name Josh Billings)
4. What men value in this world are not rights but privileges.
   H. L. Mencken (1880-1956, American journalist and essayist)
5. Tell me what you pay attention to and I will tell you who you are.
   José Ortega y Gasset
6. We do not know the true value of our moments until they have undergone the test of memory.
   Georges Duhamel
7. I had to live in the desert before I could understand the full value of grass in a green ditch.
   Ella Maillart
8. We are all special cases.
   Albert Camus

Brain Break

First Graders' Versions of the Second Half of Familiar Sayings

A first-grade teacher gave the children in her class the first half of well-known sayings and had them come up with endings.

- Children should be seen and not... spanked or grounded.
- You can't teach an old dog new... math.
- You get out of something what you... see pictured on the box.
- Don't bite the hand that... looks dirty.
- A penny saved is... not much.
- Two's company, three's... The Musketeers.
- Laugh and the whole world laughs with you, cry and... you have to blow your nose.
- If at first you don't succeed... get new batteries.

Finding Connections Exercise (See Answer #38, page 148)

Following are ten pairs of words. Your goal is to find a third word that is connected or associated with both words in each pair. This exercise will stimulate connections in your temporal lobes. The first pair is *piano* and *lock*. The answer is *key*, which is associated to both words in the pair because there are *keys* on a *piano* and you use a *key* to *lock* doors.

lock — piano	_____	river — money	_____
ship — card	_____	school — eye	_____
tree — car	_____	tennis — noise	_____
bed — paper	_____	Egyptian — mother	_____
pillow — court	_____	smoker — plumber	_____

Find a Middle Word Exercise (See Answer #39, page 148)

Find a middle word that fits after the word to the left, and in front of the word to the right, as shown in the example.

phone	*call*	girl	bear	_____	door
sail	_____	shoe	love	_____	spray
wall	_____	girl	door	_____	light
news	_____	plate	credit	_____	shark
soap	_____	towel	pine	_____	sauce

Lateral Thinking

Lateral thinking involves challenging your preconceptions and using reasoning that is not immediately obvious and may not follow a logical step-by-step approach. Problems are generally solved indirectly and creatively, using what is often referred to as "out-of-the-box" thinking. The term *lateral thinking* was popularized in 1967 by Edward de Bono.

A Problem Solved Using Lateral Thinking

Shortly after a tall office building was completed, occupants began complaining about how slow the elevators were. Management learned that redesigning the elevators was not economically feasible, but one staff member focused not on elevator performance but on the fact that people were complaining about waiting only a few minutes. He concluded that the complaints were due to boredom and suggested installing mirrors around the elevator doors on each floor so that those waiting could look at each other or themselves. The mirrors were installed quickly and at a relatively low cost, and the complaints about the slowness of the elevators stopped!

Lateral Thinking Exercises (See Answer #40, page 149)

1. Four people try to get underneath one small umbrella, but no one gets wet. How is this possible?

2. A murderer is condemned to death and must choose between three rooms. The first is full of raging fires, the second is full of lions that haven't eaten in three years, and the third is full of assassins with loaded guns. Which room is safest for him?

3. Three switches outside a windowless room are connected to three light bulbs inside the room. How can you determine which switch is connected to which bulb if you may enter the room only once?

4. Six eggs are in a basket. If six individuals each take one of the eggs, then why is one of the eggs still left in the basket.

5. My life can be measured in hours, I serve by being devoured. Thin, I am quick; fat, I am slow. Wind is my foe. What am I?

6. What can you hold in your left hand but never in your right hand?

7. Amy is standing behind Tina, and Tina is standing behind Amy. How is this possible?

8. Your doctor gives you three pills and instructs you to take one every half hour. How long will your pills last?

9. A man makes his living by watching people run home. What does he do?

10. Six drinking glasses are lined up in a row. The first three are full of water, the last three are empty. By handling and moving *only* one glass, change the arrangement so that no full glass is next to another full one, and no empty glass is next to another empty one.

Brain Break (See Answer #41, page 149)
What do you call a cow that just gave birth?

Problem Solving

Every day we deal with problems large and small. These can be "well-defined," such as calculating the cost for a room of carpeting (multiply the per square foot price by the area of the room); or "ill-defined," such as how to get from your current location to another that is 27 miles away in the next two hours when you do not have a car (ask someone for a ride, ask to borrow a car, take the train, take a taxi or bus, etc.). To solve problems, we generally use either algorithms or heuristics. *Algorithms* are strategies that always guarantee a solution (use the letter *g* in the word as a mnemonic to help you remember the definition). *Heuristics* are rules of thumb, or strategies we follow based on experience, hunches or intuition, or just common sense. They often help but can also lead us astray instead of to a solution.

There are stark differences between the way the human brain solves problems and the way computers do. For example, in the case of an anagram (AFMIA is a scrambled word), a computer would use the *algorithm* of looking at each possible arrangement of the five letters and comparing each to its lexicon (dictionary) until it found a match. The human brain knows using the algorithm would take considerable time and effort, and instead uses the *heuristic* of guessing according to knowledge of common words. Since many words begin with consonants, a person would first guess that the word probably begins with F or M, then guess that the second letter will be a vowel, so either A or I. Most likely this will be followed by another consonant, indicating that the first three letters of the word are FAM, FIM, MAF or MIF. At this point, most people would realize that the word is MAFIA.

Strategies for Solving Problems/Puzzles

1. Read carefully and try not to make any false assumptions.
2. Try to think of analogous problems/puzzles which you have already solved. This may lead to strategies for approaching the current one.
3. Use trial and error but try to be systematic and strategic.
   - For example, how many four-letter words end in the letters *ust*? A systematic approach would involve going through the alphabet and trying each letter in front of the *ust* to see if it makes a word.
   - Try working backwards, changing your perspective, rereading instructions, and/or taking a break and trying again later.
   - With jigsaw puzzles, begin with the corner and side pieces.

4. For complex problems/puzzles, attempt to break them down into simpler or smaller challenges, then solve each in turn.
5. Draw a diagram to help you visualize the problem/puzzle and its solution.
6. Look at the solution and try to see where your approach went wrong. Try to identify steps you should have taken to solve the problem/puzzle, which may help when you next encounter a similar situation.

The IDEAL Problem Solving Model (Bransford & Stein, 1984)

I = Identify the problem
D = Define and represent the problem
E = Explore possible strategies
A = Act on the strategies
L = Look back and evaluate the effects of your activities.

Problem Solving Exercises (See Answer #42, page 149)

1. Uriah Fuller, the famous Israeli psychic, can tell you the score of any baseball game before it starts. Explain how this is possible.

2. Arrange 10 equal-sized coins on the table to form a triangle. Moving only three coins, make the arrangement point in the opposite direction.

3. You've just tossed a fair coin that has come up heads for the tenth time in a row. What is the probability that it will come up heads on the next toss?

4. A traveler comes to a riverbank with a wolf, a goat, and a head of cabbage. To his chagrin, he notes that there is only one boat for crossing over, which can carry no more than two passengers—the traveler and either one of the two animals or the cabbage. As the traveler knows, if left alone together, the goat will eat the cabbage and the wolf will eat the goat. The wolf does not eat cabbage. How does the traveler transport his animals and his cabbage to the other side intact in a minimum number of back-and-forth trips? (A version of this puzzle has been found in different cultures throughout the world, and may have originated with Alcuin, who was hired by Charlemagne to create puzzles for his enjoyment.)

5. If you have black and brown socks in a drawer, mixed in a ratio of 4 to 5, and it is too dark to see them, how many socks will you have to take out of the drawer to make sure you have a *pair* of socks that are the same color?

6. A lady is celebrating her 10th birthday. On the same day her daughter, who is 20, is getting married. How can this be?

7. If it takes five minutes to boil an egg, how long will it take to boil five eggs?

8. Is it legal in the United States for a man to marry his widow's sister?

9. How many times can you subtract the number one from the number 25?

10. A farmer had seven daughters and they each had a brother. How many children did the farmer have?

11. Susan works every second day at a convenience store. Kevin also works there, but every third day. The store is open seven days a week. This week, Susan started work on Tuesday, June 1, and Kevin on Wednesday, June 2. On what date will the two work together next?

12. There are between 50 and 60 ties in a drawer. If you count them three at a time, you will find that there are two left over. If you count them five at a time, you will find that there are four left over. How many ties are in the drawer?

13. James, who is taller than Sue, is shorter than Bob. Debbie is shorter than Sue. Who is the tallest of the four?

14. A 150-foot rope is strung from the top of one flagpole to the top of another, hanging freely between them. Each flagpole is 100-feet tall. The lowest point on the rope is 25-feet above the ground. How far apart are the two flagpoles?

15. Two chess masters played fifteen consecutive games of chess. No games were drawn, every game was finished, yet both players won and lost the same number of games as each other. How could this happen?

16. What do these words have in common?
    CALMNESS   INOPERABLE   DEFER   BURST   LAUGHING   STUPID

17. The people who make it don't want it, the people who buy it don't use it, and the people who use it don't know they are using it. What is it?

Parts of the Body Exercise (See Answer #43, page 150)

For each word or phrase, name the part of the body being described (some may have more than one part that fits)

1. Where carpenters keep tools _____
2. A kind of macaroni _____
3. Part of an apple _____
4. Found on corn stalks _____
5. Coconuts grow on these _____
6. Part of a saw _____
7. Something a carpenter uses _____
8. Part of a clock _____
9. What Rover buries _____
10. Branches of a tree _____
11. A cad or a rogue _____
12. A place of worship _____
13. Weather cocks _____
14. The edge of a cup _____
15. The tortoise raced with the _____
16. Part of a river _____
17. A clam _____
18. Used on Valentine's Day _____
19. Used to cross the river _____
20. Part of an umbrella _____
21. Something to cry on _____
22. Having to do with the sea _____
23. Trendy _____
24. An accomplishment _____
25. Tug boats do this _____
26. To prepare for battle _____
27. An accusing pointer _____
28. Porcupines have more than one _____
29. Producer of veal _____
30. Add "p" to famous singer's name _____

Homonyms Exercise (See Answer #44, page 150)

For each riddle, identify a pair of words that sound the same but have different spellings and meanings.

1. If four couples went to a restaurant, how many people dined?

   _____

2. What do you say in the evening to a soldier in shining armor?

   _____

3. What is a group of musicians that isn't allowed to play?

   _____

4. What do you call a bucket that has seen a ghost?

   _____

5. If they are not here, where are they?

   _____

6. If a devil is completely sinful, what is an angel?

   _____

(Riddles from *EIGHT ATE*, ©1982 by Marvin Terban. Reprinted by permission of Clarion Books, an imprint of Houghton Mifflin Harcourt Publishing Company. All rights reserved. Used by permission.)

Word Connection Exercise (See Answer #45, page 151)

Write the appropriate word for #1. Then use the last two letters of that word as the first two letters of the next clue's answer, and do the same for each successive word.

1. The capital of California   _____
2. A burning stick to provide light   _____
3. Person in a novel or drama   _____
4. A mistake   _____
5. A musical instrument   _____
6. A large deerlike mammal   _____
7. A writing utensil   _____
8. A deceptive appearance   _____
9. Involving burdensome effort   _____
10. Typical or common   _____
11. Mammal that provides wool   _____
12. "House" in Spanish   _____
13. A Mexican dip for chips   _____
14. The capital of California   _____

Verbal and Logical Thinking Exercises (See Answer #46, page 151)

In each group of words below, one does not fit for some reason. Identify the word and why it does not fit.

1. limp, drop, like, plain, true
2. balloon, sphere, globe, cube, marble
3. scarlet, blue, crimson, coral, vermillion
4. potato, bean, squash, carrot, orange

In the exercise below, find a word that has a relationship to each of the words in the group on that line, and write the word on the blank line.

1. Eve, doctor, juice   _____
2. beast, black, skin   _____
3. cream, skate, water   _____
4. machine, space, clock   _____
5. falling, actor, dust   _____
6. gift, now, give   _____
7. hunter, hammer, gear   _____
8. pine, crab, sauce   _____
9. paint, doll, cat   _____
10. stool, powder, ball   _____
11. call, smart, pay   _____
12. flower, friend, scout   _____
13. dust, cereal, fish   _____
14. blue, cake, cottage   _____
15. baseball, panty hose, water   _____
16. mink, baked potato, peach   _____
17. courtesy, place, sense   _____
18. video, measure, worm   _____
19. ship, crawl, outer   _____
20. spot, throat, loser   _____
21. fighter, cracker, fly   _____

What Phrase is in Each Box Exercise (See Answer #47, page 152)

coORDERurt	hahandnd	<u>working</u> time
go it it it it	<u>man</u> board	<u>stand</u> I
ecnalg	you just me	he's himself
DON'T CRY SPILLED MILK	eggs easy	1. HA 3. ON 2. RM 4. NY
cycle cycle cycle	t m a u h s w t	r/e/a/d/i/n/g
TIMING TIM ING	ALONDSM PENACS PAENUTS	Pike's Peak Midnight Robert Redford
sgeg	SEARCH SEARCH	<u>January February</u> <u>March</u> DUE
over over	Hard <u>X Ahead</u>	belt hitting
me quit	HOROBOD	soil

What Phrase is in Each Box Exercise, Take Two (See Answer #48, page 153)

I RIGHT I	ALL MYSELF	CUT CUT CUT CUT
EGGS EZ	BAN ANA	LFATHERAW
JACK	NOON LAZY	ISM
2 2 2 2 2 2 2 2 DAY	XQQQME	<u>TURN</u> THE LIGHT
THE WEATHER UNDER	EVER EVER EVER EVER	POD POD POD
THEADIAMONDROUGH	<u>POWER POWER</u> △	C H O W
HEAD HEELS	PEARLSSWINE	SWEAR BIBLE BIBLE BIBLE
DICE DICE	CHAIR	E D I T
SYMPHON	OOO CIRCUS	THEFOOTDOOR

Guessing a Rule Exercise (See Answer #49, page 154)

Below are pairs of words that fit a rule; your challenge is to guess the rule.

Foot but not toe, tooth but not tongue, apple but not orange

Have you figured out the rule yet? If not, below are additional examples that fit the rule: *noodles but not rice, carrot but not tomato, book but not magazine, planner but not calendar, letter but not mail, door but not window, scissors but not knife*

Brain Break

A man went to a psychiatrist and said, "Doc, I keep having these alternating recurring dreams. First, I'm a teepee; then I'm a wigwam; then I'm a teepee; then I'm a wigwam. It's driving me crazy. What's wrong with me?"

The doctor replied: "It's very simple. You're two tents."

Creative Thinking

Creativity is often defined as the ability to come up with new and useful ideas. The creative process consists of many interacting cognitive processes (both conscious and unconscious) as well as emotions. Depending on the stage of the creative process, and *what* you're attempting to create, different brain regions work together to accomplish the task.

Functional magnetic resonance imaging (fMRI) technology allows scientists remarkable insight into brain activity. Neuroscience researchers use fMRI scans, which measure blood flow to areas of the brain, to analyze functional connectivity during creative acts. Studies have mapped brain activity across a variety of creative or artistic tasks from planning an artwork to composing poetry. Recent evidence suggests that creativity involves an interplay between the spontaneous brainstorming of ideas and the deliberate evaluation of them to determine whether they can actually work.

Creativity and the Default Mode Network

The *default mode network* is a group of brain areas that increase in activity when you are not focused on a specific task, when you are relaxed and your mind wanders. It is responsible for tasks such as imagining, daydreaming and spontaneous thinking, and may play a major role in generating ideas or thinking of possible solutions to a problem. Examples of activities in which your brain switches to default mode are showering, washing your hair, chopping vegetables, or running. Your brain is in a relaxed state and doesn't need to focus on the activity, and creative thoughts often arise. Another good time to experience insights is shortly after awakening, while your brain is still drowsy and unorganized, and therefore more open to unconventional ideas.

The *executive control network* is a set of regions that activate when you need to focus or control your thought processes. This network may be responsible for evaluating the feasibility of ideas and modifying them to fit the creative goal. The *salience network* refers to brain regions that act as a switching mechanism between the default and executive networks; it may help the brain alternate between idea generation and idea evaluation (Beaty et al., 2018).

Wallas' Model of the Creative Process

Researcher Graham Wallas (1926) described his four-stage process as follows:

1. *Preparation:* Define the problem, gather information to determine what the solution or response needs to account for, and set up criteria for evaluating the solution.
2. *Incubation:* Step back from the problem and let our minds contemplate and work it through. Like preparation, incubation can last minutes, weeks, even years.
3. *Illumination:* Allow ideas to arise from the mind and develop the basis of a creative response. These ideas can be pieces of the whole or the whole itself, i.e. seeing the entire concept or entity all at once. Illumination is often very brief, involving insight.
4. *Verification:* Carry out activities to demonstrate whether or not what emerged in illumination satisfies the need and criteria defined in the preparation stage.

Functional Fixedness

When is a hammer not a hammer? One of the greatest hindrances to creativity is cognitive rigidity. An example is the tendency to fixate on the common use of an object or its parts. We often revert to existing connections and associations and fail to "see" things other than the way we always have. Our experience may prevent us from being able to think about things in novel ways or try new approaches. To avoid functional fixedness, try to come up with unconventional uses for a conventional object. For example, a fork can be used as a fish hook, a paint scraper, or a lever for opening stubborn jars.

> *The difficulty lies not so much in developing new ideas as in escaping from old ones.*
> John Maynard Keynes

Creative Brainstorming

Pick one of these objects and think of as many uses as possible for it; then do the same for another item listed:

- *old newspapers*
- *dime*
- *old car tires*
- *cereal boxes*
- *paperclip*
- *plastic knife*
- *old cds*

SCAMS Activity

The purpose of this activity is to build fluency of thought and expression. Your task is to create five-word sentences using each letter in the word SCAMS, in order, as the first letter of each word. At first, you may only be able to think of a few sentences, but if you persist, more will occur to you. Examples include:

Seven cows are mooing softly. Senior citizens are mentally sharp.
Studious children always merit success. Singing cellos alter mood substantially.

_____
_____
_____

Expanding Associations Exercise (See Answer #50, page 154)

See how many ways you can think of to fasten two things together. List them on the lines below. (The **Answers to Exercises** chapter has a list to compare with yours.)

_____
_____
_____

Droodles for Mental Flexibility Exercise (See Answer #51, page 154)

The trademarked name "Droodle" is a nonsense word suggesting "doodle," "drawing," and "riddle." Their general form is minimal: a square box containing a few abstract pictorial elements with a caption (or several) giving a humorous explanation of the picture's subject. Try to think of several captions for each of the Droodles below. Then, look in the *Answers to Exercises* Chapter to see what captions were published with the Droodles.

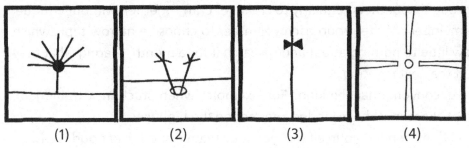

(1)   (2)   (3)   (4)

(Excerpted from *Droodles – The Classic Collection* Copyright ©2000 by Tallfellow Press. All Rights Reserved. Used by Permission.)

_____

_____

_____

_____

_____

_____

For an additional creativity exercise, create your own Droodles and ask others to think of captions for them.

Practice Divergent Thinking

1. Try to think of ways in which the world would be different if some conditions were altered, like if humans all had six fingers.
2. Pick two random nouns and try to use the fewest words to connect the first word to the second. Examples for fish…money could be water and liquidity, or shark and loan.

Additional Ideas for Creative Thinking

1. Use a line from a poem or three random items to stimulate your imagination for writing lyrics for a song.
2. Describe an idea for a television show which would attract a large audience but has not yet been tried.
3. Pick three magazine pictures at random and write a story about them. Pick a word randomly from the dictionary, and let it inspire a drawing or sculpture.
4. Form a group that gathers regularly to create or craft together, without critique. Or have members of the group each volunteer to choose a narrow topic which they know little to nothing about and research it for a month, sharing what they learned at the next meeting.
5. Cultivate unconventional thinking. For example, when stuck in a traffic jam, decide that aliens must have landed and melted the highway.
6. Use affirmations: remind yourself that you are creative and full of good ideas.
7. Don't be afraid to fail, or even to produce something mediocre.

Answers to Exercises

Chapter One

Answer #1 Brain Break

Brain riddles:

1. *Gives a brain wave.*
2. *Thanks for the memories.*
3. *A bright idea.*
4. *They like to send and receive a lot of messages.*
5. *Perform PET scans.*

Chapter Four

Answer #2 *TOT (Tip-of-the-Tongue) Exercise*

1. geode
2. longitude
3. deciduous
4. charisma
5. hemoglobin
6. hieroglyphics
7. barnacle
8. surrogate

Answer #3 *States and Capitals Exercise*

Arizona – Phoenix

California – Sacramento

Nevada – Carson City

New York – Albany

Ohio – Columbus

Pennsylvania – Harrisburg

Rhode Island – Providence

Texas – Austin

Chapter Five

Answer #4 *Sudoku*

2	3	4	1
4	1	3	2
1	4	2	3
3	2	1	4

4	1	2	3
3	2	4	1
1	4	3	2
2	3	1	4

3	4	1	2
1	2	3	4
4	3	2	1
2	1	4	3

5	6	4	2	1	3	1	2	3	5	4	6
1	2	3	6	4	5	4	6	5	2	1	3
4	3	5	1	6	2	5	4	6	3	2	1
6	1	2	3	5	4	3	1	2	4	6	5
2	4	6	5	3	1	2	3	1	6	5	4
3	5	1	4	2	6	6	5	4	1	3	2

Answer #5 *Anagrams Exercise*

It is important to use your brain and **STIMULATE** it with new and **COMPLEX** ideas. Even the brains of **OLDER** adults can **LEARN** and grow, especially when doing **MENTAL** exercise like **SOLVING** anagrams. These are just some of the things you can do to build cognitive **RESERVE**.

Answer #6 *Rearrange and Categorize Exercises*

The second and fourth anagrams can be rearranged to form **NATURE** and **ENGINE**
The words are: **BRAIN, AGING, STRATEGIES, PROBLEM**
COPENHAGEN (not in North America, as are **CHICAGO, TORONTO, and MIAMI**)
SHANGHAI fits in the category *city*

Answer #7 *Musical Instrument Anagrams*

1. BANJO
2. UKULELE
3. VIOLIN
4. FLUTE
5. XYLOPHONE
6. CLARINET
7. GUITAR
8. TROMBONE

Answer #8 *Name List Recall Exercise*

1. Chronological order: Johnson, Nixon, Ford, Carter, Reagan, Bush, Clinton, Bush, Obama, Trump
2. Democrats: Johnson, Carter, Clinton, Obama
   Republicans: Nixon, Ford, Reagan, Bush, Bush, Trump
3. Alphabetical order: Bush, Bush, Carter, Clinton, Ford, Johnson, Nixon, Obama, Reagan, Trump

Answer #9 *Visualization Exercise*

1. right hand
2. no
3. round or circular
4. spinach

Chapter Six

Answer #10 *Word Riddles Exercise*

1. envelope
2. mushroom, broom, any word that has the letters *room* in it
3. x
4. t
5. electrician

Answer #11 *Item Attributes Exercise*

The three items all have body part words in common: *ears, teeth, and eye.*

Answer #12 *Attention to Detail Exercise*

The solution is that there was poison in the ice cubes, so as they melted, it poisoned the drink. Bob drank his quickly *before* the ice melted, so very little poison had a chance to get into the drink. Bart drank slowly, allowing the poison to get into the drink as the ice cubes melted.

Answer #13 *Paying Attention and Following Instructions*

1. N E V E R T O O O L D
2. E V E R T O O O L D N
3. E V R T O L D N
4. T O E V R L D N
5. T O L E V R D N
6. T O L E A R D N
7. T O L E A R N

Answer #14 *Can You Find 12 Differences*

Giraffe Pictures	Burro Pictures	Handyman Pictures
Small leaf at right of tree colored in.	Buckle on saddle is missing.	Carpenter's side pocket is missing.
Nose line on left giraffe removed.	Tree on horizon is missing.	Light bulb in lamp is missing.
Shadow on lower left coconut removed.	Flower on cactus is missing.	Drawer handle is missing.
Leaf vein below gecko removed.	Top of sombrero is colored in.	Chest pocket is colored in.
Ear line on left giraffe removed.	Top of saddle pattern is colored in.	Carpenter square is longer.
Bottom spot on right giraffe colored in.	Top of pyramid is colored in.	Elbow on lamp arm is colored in.
Top tree leaf removed.	Cactus has moved.	Pant cuff is colored in.
Horn on right giraffe moved.	Top leaf on branch at left has moved.	Hole in board has moved down.
Spot on left giraffe moved.	Brim on sombrero is wider.	Bottom drawer is narrower.
Branch on left side shorter.	Strip on shirt sleeve is taller.	Screwdrivers have moved.
Gecko tail longer.	Rope is longer.	Tall jar has moved.
Gecko eye missing.	Walking cane is taller.	Top of hat is colored in.

Chapter Seven

Answer #15 *Name that Thing (below are examples of possible answers)*

Name an animal that *begins* with letter	C	**camel, cow**
A fish	S	**salmon**
A bird	E	**eagle**
A vegetable	P	**pea, pepper, potato**
A profession	D	**doctor, dentist**
An article of clothing	T	**tie, trousers**
A country	I	**India, Ireland**
A city	N	**Nashville, New York**
A state	A	**Alabama, Arkansas, Alaska**
A planet	M	**Mars, Mercury**

Name that Thing (*below are examples of possible answers*)

Name an animal that *ends* with letter	E	horse, bee
A fish	A	tuna
A bird	W	sparrow
A vegetable	H	spinach
A profession	Y	hockey, psychology, taxidermy
An article of clothing	T	hat, coat, jacket
A country	D	England, Ireland
A city	O	Chicago, Toronto, Oslo
A state	S	Illinois, Texas, Arkansas
A planet	H	Earth

Answer #16 *Find Words Ending in ...ration*

Of homage	*adoration*
Surgery	operation
A party or fete	celebration
Deliverance	liberation
Of kindness	consideration
A pardoning	exoneration
Tuning adjustment	calibration
Company	corporation

Answer #17 *Find Words Ending in...ace*

The ace which supports	*brace*
A small quantity	trace
Fine open fabric	lace
Unoccupied area	space
A competition	race
A rate of speed	pace
Dishonor	disgrace
Obliterate	efface
A visage	face
Lose something	misplace
To clasp	embrace
Elegance	grace

Answer #18 *Find Words Ending in...age*

The age which binds	*bandage*
Someone wise	**sage**
Of the theater	**stage**
Bravery	**courage**
Captive	**hostage**
Part of a book	**page**
To betroth	**engage**
Of intense anger	**rage**
Of leaves	**foliage**
Of matrimony	**marriage**

Answer #19 *Find Words Ending in ...ice*

Cost of something	*price*
Liquid from fruit	**juice**
Option or selection	**choice**
Guidance	**advice**
Lack of bravery	**cowardice**
Lack of fairness	**injustice**
Ill will, evil intention	**malice**
Preconceived opinion	**prejudice**
Crime conspirator	**accomplice**
Student learning trade	**apprentice**

Answer #20 *Find Words Ending in ...ise*

Thoughtfully plan/invent	*devise*
Ideal/idyllic place	**paradise**
Promote product/service/event	**advertise**
Rebuke/reprimand severely	**chastise**
Cut foreskin off	**circumcise**
Activity to improve fitness	**exercise**
Create/perform spontaneously	**improvise**
Direct execution of task/project	**supervise**
Goods to be bought and sold	**merchandise**
Way to settle a dispute	**compromise**

Answer #21 *Find Words Ending in ...ight*

Impressive power/strength	**might**
Heaviness of person/thing	**weight**
Plant disease	**blight**
Measurement from base to top	**height**
Right of possession from birth	**birthright**
Great pleasure	**delight**
Movement through air	**flight**
Ability to see	**sight**
Extending in one direction	**straight**
Understanding situation after	**hindsight**

Answer #22 *Find Words Ending in ...ury*

Put or hide under ground	**bury**
State of extravagance	**luxury**
Telling a lie under oath	**perjury**
Heavy silvery-white metal	**mercury**
Revenue/funds of government	**treasury**
Hurt or damage	**injury**
Charging unreasonable interest	**usury**
Period of one hundred years	**century**
Wild or violent anger	**fury**
Indigence, extreme poverty	**penury**

Answer #23 *Phonological Fluency Exercises*

Examples include *shoes, socks, sandals, sneakers, slippers, skis, skates, snow-shoes, stockings, stilts, stilettos, snowboard, sunscreen, salve.*

Answer #24 *Misspelled Items Grocery List Exercise*

tear **pear**	soap **soup**	gun **gum gin bun**
fork **pork**	break **bread**	beach **peach**
steam **steak**	coin **corn**	dream **cream**
mile **milk**	lake **cake**	dish **fish**

Chapter Eight

Answer #25 Brain Break *Match the "punny" ending to the proper beginning*
1.f 2.a 3.e 4.c 5.b 6.d

Answer #26 *Spelling Elaboration Exercise – possible examples*

already	**AL is READY! (to remember there is only one l)**
believe	Never beLIEve a LIE.
chauffeur	Our chauffEUR hates the traffic in EURope.
forty	**A gift FOR TY, who is forty today!**
inoculation	**When you get an INoculation, the needle goes IN your skin.**
outrageous	**She flew into a RAGE at the outRAGEous suggestion.**
parallel	Draw ALL the lines parALLel.
plague	**There was a plaGUE of GLUE.**
principal	The princiPAL is your PAL.
stationery	**We write a lettER on stationERy.**

Answer #27 *Vocabulary Elaboration Exercise – possible examples*

aberrant (to stray from the right or usual course)	*A bear ran* (aberrant) **off the course.**
altruism (unselfish concern for others)	**It's ALl TRU, U come before I.**
delta (land at the mouth of a river)	**The *Delta* airplane crashed at the *mouth* of the river.**
truculent (fierce, cruel, savagely brutal)	**That *truck you lent* me ran me over!**
winsome (sweetly or innocently charming, engaging)	**His *winsome* ways will WIN SOME hearts!**

Answer #28 *States and Capitals Exercise – possible examples*

Little Rock, Arkansas	**Picture someone sawing a rock, saying "I can saw a little rock."**
Tallahassee, Florida	**Since "lassie" can mean a girl, picture a tall girl (tall lassie) on the beach (Florida).**
Augusta, Maine	A *gust of* wind blew through my horse's *mane*.
Helena, Montana	A girl named *Helena* is climbing a *mountain*.
Harrisburg, Pennsylvania	**Picture a hairy burger (Harrisburg) with a pencil through it (Pennsylvania).**
Cheyenne, Wyoming	**Picture a shy girl named Anne (Cheyenne) on a ranch in Wyoming.**

Answer #29 *Story Elaboration Exercise – One Example*

A lady from **Delaware** bought a ticket on the **Pennsylvania** railroad. She packed a **new jersey** sweater in her suitcase and went to visit her friend **Georgia** in **Connecticut**. The next morning, she and her friend attended **mass** in a church on **Mary's land**. Then they took the **South car line** home, and dined on a **new ham**, which had been roasted by **Virginia** (the cook from **New York**). After dinner they took the **North car line** and **rode to the island**.

Answer #30 *Prospective Memory Exercise – Possible Strategies*

1. Place Susan's book by your door or in your car, so you will see it before you go to meet her for dinner.
2. Make a note on your calendar or planner to mail the birthday card on the date you need to so it will arrive in time for George's birthday.
3. Set an alarm on your smart phone to go off about at noon tomorrow to remind you to meet Harry and Gladys for lunch at the Bistro at 12:30.
4. Move a ring to your other hand, or move your watch to your other wrist, and when you do that, tell yourself it is to remind you to schedule your next doctor appointment when you get home.

Answer #31 *Organizing and Categorizing Grocery List Recall Exercise*

Dairy – milk, eggs, butter, yogurt
Meats – ground beef, chicken, bacon, pork roast
Frozen – ice cream, popsicles, frozen corn, toaster waffles

Answer #32 *Everyday Memory Exercises*

1. (a) For dinner we ate *frozen pizza* with *lettuce* and *carrots*, but instead of eating his *cat food*, our cat got into the pantry and ate some *crackers* and *corn flakes*! We used *laundry detergent* and *toilet paper* to clean up the mess.

1. (b) As I walk into the living room, I see *toilet paper* wrapped around the lampshade, a *frozen pizza* on the sofa, a *carrot* sticking out of a head of *lettuce* on the coffee table, *crackers* and *corn flakes* on the end table, a bottle of *laundry detergent* on the recliner, and a bowl of *cat food* on the piano bench.

2. When the waitress says her name, make sure you pay attention to what she looks like; notice her height, hair color/style, and other things about her appearance. Use the strategies for remembering names (visualize her name in writing when she says it, repeat it to yourself, use it out loud when addressing her, associate her name with someone you know with the same name, and/or think of an image for her name and connect it with something about her appearance, etc.).

3. Before going to the amusement park, make a list of the areas you want to show your relatives and create an *acronym* with the first letter of each, or a *sentence* in which the first letter of each word stands for one of the attractions or areas.

4. Ask your friends to repeat the jokes and try to memorize the punch line, since it generally doesn't follow in a natural sequence. Then later you can work back from that into the joke set-up. *Personalize* the joke by *visualizing* the scenario as a familiar place and think of someone you know as the star of the joke. Use *repetition;* practice the joke numerous times before trying it in front of others.

5. Create an image that includes all four announcements. For example, visualize a calendar turned to October, and in the square for 15 see a large pot. Sticking out of the pot are two books, a cup of coffee with a dollar bill in it, and an invitation.

6. Create an image that will remind you of the five errands. For example, visualize yourself wearing a suit covered in stamps, with the dry-cleaning plastic bag still attached. You are entering the hospital, where you see your friend wearing large red-rimmed glasses and holding a present wrapped in bright blue paper. (Remember the *ACE* strategy for images: Action, Color, Exaggeration.)

7. When your new acquaintance tells you her phone number, try to learn it in chunks of three, three, and four digits. If the area code is the same as yours, you only need to learn the last seven digits. If it is not, try to visualize the digits in each chunk, perhaps in bright purple on white paper, and as larger three- and four-digit numbers rather than as seven individual digits. Look for numerical patterns *in* or possible associations *to* each chunk. For example, visualize a dozen eggs for 12, a clock face showing 5:05 for 505, boiling water for 212, a jumbo jet for 747, Columbus for 1492, etc.

Chapter Nine

Answer #33 *Continuing Patterns Exercise*

aabccdeef...***ggh***

acegi...***kmo***

zyxwv...***uts***

O, T, T, F, F, S, S, ...***E, N, T*** (for eight, nine, ten)

5, 8, 12, 15, 19, 22, 26...**29, 33, 36, 40 (alternate adding 3 or 4 to the previous number)**

1, 2, 3, 5, 8, 13, 21, 34...**55, 89, 144, 233 (add the previous two numbers to get the next one in the sequence)**

18, 20, 24, 30, 38,...**48, 60 (add 2, then 4, then 6, then 8, then 10, then 12, etc.)**

Answer #34 *Finding Patterns Exercise*

Things that are blue	759 **SKY**	53267 **JEANS**	62326 **OCEAN**
Things that are round	2255 **BALL**	247253 **CIRCLE**	288866 **BUTTON**
Vegetables	7327 **PEAS**	778274 **SQUASH**	27622654 **BROCCOLI**
Dogs	766353 **POODLE**	265543 **COLLIE**	32724863 **DASCHUND**

Answer #35 *Spatial Reasoning Exercises*

In the 4 x 4 grid, there are 30 squares.

In a 3 x 3 x 3 cube there are:

8 blocks with 3 sides painted.

12 blocks with 2 sides painted.

6 blocks with 1 side painted.

1 block with 0 sides painted (not visible, in center of cube).

Answer #36 *Ordering Exercise*

One possible way to order the names according to the rule are:

CAREY, SCOTT, MADISON, WILLIAM, HOWARD, EDITH, NICOLE, LOGAN

Answer #37 *Reason These Out Exercise*

1. C. Even though we know Aaron is an adult, we know nothing about Nicole.
2. The solution is to multiply the previous number by 3 and add 1, so $n = 364$.
3. Most people respond that the tie costs $5, but this does not satisfy the requirements given. If the tie costs $5 and the shirt costs $50 *more than the tie*, *together* they would cost *more* than $55. The correct answer is that the tie costs $2.50.
4. The best way to reason this out is by using *analogy*: it is basically the same as 2, but with different items and amounts. The correct answer is that the ball costs 5 cents.

Answer #38 *Finding Connections Exercise*

lock — piano	**key**	river — money	**bank, flow**
ship — card	**deck**	school — eye	**pupil, exam**
tree — car	**trunk**	tennis — noise	**racket**
bed — paper	**sheet**	Egyptian — mother	**mummy**
pillow — court	**case**	smoker — plumber	**pipe**

Answer #39 *Find a Middle Word Exercise*

phone	*call*	girl	bear	*trap*	door
sail	*boat*	shoe	love	*bug*	spray
wall	*flower*	girl	door	*stop*	light
news	*paper*	plate	credit	*card*	shark
soap	*dish*	towel	pine	*apple*	sauce

Answer #40 *Lateral Thinking Exercises*

1. It's not raining! (This is an example of mindlessness.)
2. Lions that haven't eaten in three years are most likely dead, so that room is safest.
3. Switch one light on for a minute; turn it off and turn on the second. Go inside the room and feel the off-bulbs. The warm one is connected to the first switch; the bulb that is on is connected to the second switch.
4. The person who took the last egg took it *in* the basket.
5. A candle
6. Your right hand
7. They are standing back to back.
8. Your pills will last one hour, since you take one immediately, one a half hour later, and the third at the end of the hour.
9. He is a home plate umpire.
10. Pour the water from the second glass into the fifth glass, which is empty. Then every other glass will be full of water.

Answer #41 Brain Break
Decaffeinated! (De-calf-inated)

Answer #42 *Problem Solving Exercises*

1. The score of any game before it starts is *zero to zero*.
2. Move the coin at the right tip to the left of the column of 4, then move the top and bottom coins from that column of four to the row of 2, creating the opposite arrangement.
3. The probability of a coin coming up heads is always 50%.
4. He should take the goat over first, then come back for the wolf, but when he deposits the *wolf on the other side, he will need to bring back the goat. Then he can take the cabbage* across, leaving it safely with the wolf while he goes back to fetch the goat. *Not recognizing that you may have to undo a step already taken can be a hindrance.*
5. The minimum number you have to take out is 3. The ratio is *irrelevant information* and should be ignored. *Irrelevant information is a hindrance.*
6. She was born in leap year; notice it does not say she is 10 years old, merely that she is celebrating her 10th birthday.
7. Five minutes.

8. No, because if he has a widow, he is dead.

9. Once, because after you subtract 1 from 25, the next time you will be subtracting it from 24.

10. Eight: seven daughters and one son

11. June 5

12. 59. Counting 5 at a time with 4 left over means there must be either 54 or 59. Divide each by 3, and the one that gives you a remainder of 2 is 59.

13. Bob

14. The flagpoles are next to each other.

15. They were not playing against each other.

16. Each word contains three letters in correct alphabetical order.

17. A coffin.

Answer #43 *Parts of the Body Exercise*

1. chest	11. heel	21. shoulder
2. elbow	12. temple	22. navel (naval)
3. core or skin	13. veins (vanes)	23. hip
4. ears	14. lip	24. feet (feat)
5. palms	15. hair (hare)	25. toe (tow)
6. teeth	16. mouth	26. arm
7. nail	17. muscle (mussel)	27. finger
8. hand or face	18. heart	28. spine
9. bone	19. bridge	29. calf
10. limbs	20. rib	30. pelvis

Answer #44 *Homonyms Exercise*

1. EIGHT ATE
2. NIGHT KNIGHT
3. BANNED BAND
4. PALE PAIL
5. THEY'RE THERE
6. WHOLLY HOLY

Answer #45 *Word Connection Exercise*

1. Sacramento
2. torch
3. character
4. error
5. organ
6. antelope
7. pencil
8. illusion
9. onerous
10. usual
11. alpaca
12. casa
13. salsa
14. Sacramento

Answer #46 *Verbal and Logical Thinking Exercises*

The word that doesn't fit with the others, and the reason:

1. *plain* has five letters
2. *cube* is not spherical
3. *blue* is not a shade of red
4. *orange* is not a vegetable

The word that has a relationship to each of the words in the group on that line:

1. apple
2. beauty
3. ice
4. time
5. star
6. present
7. head
8. apple
9. house
10. foot
11. phone
12. girl
13. bowl
14. cheese
15. runs
16. skin
17. common
18. tape
19. space
20. sore
21. fire

Answer #47 *What Phrase is in Each Box Exercise*

coORDERurt **order in the court**	hahandnd **hand in hand**	<u>working</u> time **working overtime**
go it it it it **go for it**	<u>man</u> board **man overboard**	<u>stand</u> I **I understand**
ecnalg **backward glance**	you just me **just between you and me**	he's himself **he's beside himself**
DON'T CRY SPILLED MILK **don't cry over spilled milk**	eggs easy **eggs over easy**	1. HA 3. ON 2. RM 4. NY **four-part harmony**
cycle cycle cycle **tricycle**	t m a u h s w t **what goes up must come down**	r/e/a/d/i/n/g **reading between the lines**
TIMING TIM ING **split second timing**	ALONDSM PENACS PAENUTS **mixed nuts**	Pike's Peak Midnight Robert Redford **tall dark and handsome**
sgeg **scrambled eggs**	SEARCH **search high and low** SEARCH	<u>January February March</u> DUE **three months overdue**
over over **left overs**	Hard <u>X Ahead</u> **hard times ahead**	belt hitting **hitting below the belt**
me quit **quit following me**	HOROBOD **Robin Hood**	soil **top soil**

Answer #48 *What Phrase is in Each Box Exercise, Take Two*

I RIGHT I **right between the eyes**	ALL MYSELF **all by myself**	CUT CUT CUT CUT **cut corners**
EGGS EZ **eggs over easy**	BAN ANA **banana split**	LFATHERAW **father-in-law**
JACK **Jack in the box**	NOON LAZY **lazy afternoon**	ISM **capitalism**
2 2 2 2 2 2 2 2 DAY **Tuesday**	XQQQME **excuse me**	<u>TURN</u> THE LIGHT **turn on the light**
THE WEATHER UNDER **under the weather**	EVER EVER EVER EVER **forever**	POD POD POD **tripod**
THEADIAMONDROUGH **a diamond in the rough**	<u>POWER POWER</u> △ **balance of power**	C H O W **chow down**
HEAD HEELS **head over heels**	PEARLSSWINE **pearls before swine**	SWEAR BIBLE BIBLE BIBLE **swear on a stack of** **Bibles**
DICE DICE **paradise**	CHAIR **high chair**	E D I T **rising tide**
SYMPHON **unfinished symphony**	OOO CIRCUS **three-ring circus**	THEFOOTDOOR **foot in the door**

Answer #49 *Guessing a Rule Exercise*
The rule is that it *is* words that have double letters in them, and *not* words that don't. Examples: *noodles but not rice, carrot but not tomato, book but not magazine, planner but not calendar, letter but not mail, door but not window, scissors but not knife*

Answer #50 *Expanding Associations Exercise*
A few could include: glue, paper clip, gum, paste, tape, staple, button and button hole, Velcro, buckle, clip, weld, sew, cement, clasp, snap, hook and eye. There are probably more.

Answer #51 *Droodles*
The actual captions of the Droodles are:
(1) Spider doing a handstand.
(2) An early bird who caught a very strong worm.
(3) Man in tuxedo who stood too close to the front of an elevator.
(4) Four elephants inspecting a grapefruit.
Excerpted from *Droodles – The Classic Collection* ©2000 by Tallfellow Press. All Rights Reserved. Used by Permission.

Books for Further Reading

NOTE: References for research journal articles cited in this book can be found at the author's website: www.brainandmemoryhealth.com

Alloway, T. (2013). *The Working Memory Advantage*. NY: Simon and Schuster.

Amen, D. (2017). *Memory Rescue: Supercharge Your Brain, Reverse Memory Loss, and Remember What Matters Most.* Carol Stream, IL: Tyndale Momentum.

Anderson, N. D., Murphy, K.J., & Troyer, A.K. (2012). *Living with mild cognitive impairment*. Oxford: Oxford University Press.

Bragdon, A. D. (2011). *Brain Games*. NY: Skyhorse Publishing.

Bransford, J.D., & Stein, B.S. (1984). *The IDEAL Problem Solver*. NY: W.H. Freeman & Co.

Carson, S. (2010). *Your Creative Brain: Seven Steps to Maximize Imagination, Productivity, and Innovation in Your Life*. San Francisco: Jossey-Bass.

Chernow, F.B. (1997). *The Sharper Mind.* NJ: Prentice Hall.

Danesi, M. (2011). *Extreme Brain Workout: 500 Fun and Challenging Puzzles to Boost Your Brain Power*. Ontario, Canada: Harlequin.

Danesi, M. (2009). *The Total Brain Workout: 450 Puzzles to Sharpen Your Mind, Improve Your Memory & Keep Your Brain Fit*. Ontario, Canada: Harlequin.

Editors. (2007). *Brain Games #1: Lower Your Brain Age in Minutes a Day*. Lincolnwood, IL Publications International Ltd.

Editors. (2008). *Brain Games Picture Puzzles: How Many Differences Can You Find? No.5*. Morton Grove, IL. Publications International Ltd.

Emmons, H., & Alter, D. (2015). *Staying Sharp: 9 Keys for a Youthful Brain through Modern Science and Ageless Wisdom*. NY: Touchstone.

Fotuhi, M. (2013). *Boost Your Brain: The New Art and Science Behind Enhanced Brain Performance*. NY: Harper Collins.

Grierson, B. (2015). *What Makes Olga Run? The Mystery of the 90-Something Track Star and What She Can Teach Us About Living Longer, Happier Lives*. NY: Henry Holt and Co.

Henner, M. (2013). *Total Memory Makeover: Uncover Your Past, Take Charge of Your Future*. NY: Gallery Books.

Higbee, K.L. (2001). *Your Memory: How It Works and How to Improve It*. NY: Marlowe & Company.

Huffington, A. (2016). *The Sleep Revolution: Transforming Your Life, One Night at a Time*. NY: Harmony Books.

Linde, N. (2012). *399 Games, Puzzles & Trivia Challenges Specially Designed to Keep Your Brain Young*. NY: Workman Publishing.

Loftus, E.F. (1979). *Eyewitness testimony*. Cambridge, MA: Harvard University Press.

Maas, J.B. (2011). *Sleep for Success! Everything You Must Know about Sleep but Are Too Tired to Ask*. Bloomington, IN: AuthorHouse.

Macknik, S., & Martinez-Conde, S. (2010). *Sleights of Mind: What the Neuroscience of Magic Reveals about Our Everyday Deceptions*. NY: Henry Holt and Company.

Mednick, S.C. (2006). *Take a Nap! Change Your Life: The Scientific Plan to Make You Smarter, Healthier, More Productive.* NY: Workman Publishing.

Michelon, P. (2012). *Max Your Memory*. NY: DK Publishing.

Price, R. (2019). *The Ultimate Droodles Compendium*. CA: Tallfellow Press.

Ratey, J. (2008). *Spark: The Revolutionary New Science of Exercise and the Brain*. NY: Little, Brown and Company.

Restak, R., & Kim, S. (2010). *The Playful Brain: The Surprising Science of How Puzzles Improve Your Mind.* NY: Riverhead Books.

Schacter, D.L. (2001). *The Seven Sins of Memory*. NY: Houghton Mifflin.

Sciandra, K. (2015). *The Mindfulness Habit*. Woodbury, MN: Llewellyn Publications.

Small, G., & Vorgan, G. (2008). *iBrain: Surviving the Technological Alteration of the Modern Mind.* NY: Harper Collins.

Wallas, G. (1926). *The Art of Thought*. London, UK: Jonathan Cape.

Acknowledgements

I am indebted to many people for their help and inspiration in producing this book. I would like to thank Carole Mazurowski Orr, Ph.D., former journalist and retired neuropsychologist, who cogently edited and gave input on the content. I am grateful to my husband Carey who, though an electrical engineer, has a better command of Word than I do, and helped me organize and format the structure of the book, as well as doing a most thorough proofreading! My children Scott and Nicole, when asked, shared their opinions on various aspects of the design. Several friends and colleagues encouraged me throughout the writing, and I am especially grateful to Howard Posner, who read the manuscript and provided detailed feedback.

About the Author

Linda earned her Ph.D. from the University of Colorado at Boulder, where she conducted her dissertation research on memory. She served on the undergraduate and graduate faculties of Wheaton College and Judson University, teaching educational and cognitive psychology. For her sabbatical research, she conducted a national survey on brain health.

As the owner of *Brain and Memory Health*, Linda presents regularly at various conferences and is a national speaker for marketing events and for residents at senior living communities. Her topics include brain fitness, maximizing memory and productivity, using memory to write memoir, and enhancing emotional intelligence. She also facilitates continuing education workshops for healthcare professionals.

In 2015 she published *BE! Brain Enrichment*, a curriculum designed to help people learn about brain health and improve their cognitive skills. The *BE!* course continues to be taught at numerous senior living communities and senior centers throughout the United States, and the positive response to it from facilitators and participants prompted her to write this book.

Through her business Dr. Sasser exercises her passion for educating and motivating people to fully utilize their brain's potential.

Her website is www.brainandmemoryhealth.com

Contact her at linda@brainandmemoryhealth.com

Made in the USA
Monee, IL
12 January 2025

76665906R10092